Restored!
Embracing Weight Loss God's Way

Helen Thomas Baratta

Treasured Temple

Praise for

Restored! Embracing Weight Loss God's Way
and
Helen Thomas Baratta

This is not another diet book. It's about first finding peace with God *then* losing the weight. Honest and transparent, the author freely shares her emotional pain and numerous weight loss failures—but more importantly, how she overcame over-eating through her relationship with Jesus. Once the true beauty of her inner life was revealed, she was able to reach and maintain a healthy weight.

—*Joel Comiskey, PhD, President of Joel Comiskey Group*

Helen has coached thousands worldwide, inspiring others to discover the practical steps to health— empowered with God's help, moment by moment, bite by bite.

—*Pam Farrel, author of* **Men are Like Waffles, Women are Like Spaghetti** *and* **7 Simple Skills for Every Woman: Success In Keeping It All Together**

Helen is dedicated to health, wellness and excellence. She will have you feeling like you can reach any goal.

—*Beth Caldwell, Founder of Leadership Academy for Women*

For years, I've watched Helen inspire, disciple and encourage people toward a healthy, balanced and Christ-like life. This book will likewise draw you toward the life that God created you to live.

—*Steve Cordle, Lead Pastor of Crossroads Church*

From a successful businesswoman who had life all figured out except the weight issue, the author takes us on a powerful journey to health. Read this book and restore your life, too.

—*Karen Porter, author, speaker, coach and publisher*

A powerful book! Helen shares it all—from her less-than- perfect childhood to hopeless attempts at weight loss. Finally, God's relentless pursuit and love motivated her to change her life forever. Whether you want to lose those last 10 pounds or need a complete body-mind- spirit overhaul, this book will inspire you to not give up on yourself or God.

—*Vicki Heath, author, speaker, coach and National Director of First Place 4 Health*

Helen has succeeded in capturing what it takes to achieve a balanced lifestyle. This book will help you do the same if you take its truths to heart.

—*Carole Lewis, Director Emeritus of First Place 4 Health and author of* **Live Life Right Here Right Now**

This book is real, relevant and will transform your health.

—*Steve Reynolds, Senior Pastor of Capital Baptist Church, Annandale, Virginia and author of* **Bod4God: Twelve Weeks to Lasting Weight Loss.**

Restored!

Embracing
Weight Loss
God's Way

Helen Thomas Baratta

Restored! Embracing Weight Loss God's Way
© 2017 by Helen Thomas Baratta

ISBN-13: 978-0-9978865-0-4

Treasured Temple Publications
PO Box 383421
Waikoloa, HI 96738
www.helenbaratta.com

Editor: Gina Mazza (ginamazza.com)
Cover Design and Interior Layout: Lee Ann Fortunato-Heltzel (creativeonemarketing.com)

They are like a man building a house,
who dug down deep and laid the foundation on rock.
When a flood came, the torrent struck that house but could not shake it,
because it was well built. (Luke 6:48)

First, I dedicate this book to my God, who is my strength and salvation. Apart from You, I cannot do anything. I will do whatever you want me to do.

Dedication

The Lord is my strength and my defense; he has become my salvation. He is my God, and I will praise him, my father's God, and I will exalt him. (Exodus 15:2)

Second, I dedicate this book to Vince, my husband and partner in life. I will love you all the days of my life.

He is like a tree planted by streams of water that yields its fruit in its season, and its leaf does not wither. In all that he does, he prospers. (Psalm 1:3)

Third, I dedicate this book to my sons, Alex and Davis, who provide me with joy and inspiration. I will pray for you and do my best to set an example for you.

I have no greater joy than to hear that my children are walking in the truth. (3 John 1:4)

I owe a debt of love and gratitude to those who have contributed to the process of writing this book in words, thoughts and prayers. It has been a joy and privilege to be part of the Lord's plan and purpose, as He brought together encouragement and support for this book to be written and shared.

Special thanks to Ann Terputac, Karen Evans Meyers, Mark Belko and Sue Neeley for painstakingly copyediting the initial drafts. I appreciate their timely review and recommendations, and thank them for both their kind words notated in the margins and prayers throughout the project.

Acknowledgements

Larry Leach, my writing coach, taught me the difference between "show" and "tell." He spent a year with me as I made revisions chapter by chapter. Larry gave me the confidence to share my words with others.

Gina Mazza, my primary editor, guided me in clarifying the book's premise and organizing the content. She helped me to see that I am, in essence, leading readers to a spiritual solution for what is perceived as a physical problem. I am grateful for Gina's expertise.

I am thankful for the pastors, leaders and mentors who have left an indelible mark on my life: Al Gyergyo, Carole Lewis, Delilah Dirksen, Gerry Wakeland, James Roberts, Jane Dotter, Jennifer Krogh, Joel Comiskey, Joyce Ainsworth, Karen Porter, Lisa Lewis, RJ Scherba, Steve Cordle, Sue Neeley, Vicki Heath and all the faithful leaders at First Place 4 Health.

I give thanks to both of my sisters, Kathy and Cyndi, who are entwined in these pages, have provided insight and helped me recall some of the darkest days of our lives. My mom, with whom I Skype weekly, blessed me with permission to share whatever is necessary to help others heal. To my two stepbrothers, who were innocent bystanders when they joined our crazy family.

Last but not least, special thanks to the three men in my life who challenge me to be my best. Vince, Alex and Davis, thank you for loving me regardless of the shape I'm in, both inside or out.

Contents

PART TWO: ROUGH SAND, STRIP AND REVEAL THE SUB-LAYERS

PART THREE: BUFF, PROTECT AND PRESERVE THE RESTORATION

I didn't realize that I was a fat kid until I experienced my first week of summer camp at the age of 11. My mom recalls me coming home from that camp covered in hundreds of mosquito bites, but what I remember is being ridiculed as "fat" by some of the other campers. The camp counselor used me as an example during a sit down.

"You guys, like Alex!" he said in front of the whole cabin, "He's funny, he's fat, and you should be okay with that."

Foreword

From that point on, I sort of leaned into "being fat." I didn't really consider getting exercise or "eating right" through middle and high school outside of being in marching band and carrying a sousaphone. I never liked gym class, wasn't particularly good at sports, and generally surrounded myself with others who weren't either.

I lost some weight in college due to crash dieting when I became much more self-conscious about how I looked to girls. I dropped from 260 to 215 and thought I looked great even though I was pretty much starving myself to gain these results. That weight crept back relatively fast and kept climbing after graduation. I landed my first real job and moved out of my parent's house. I would go out for drinks and dine out, without a calorie of concern towards what was good for me.

Then three things happened: my mom achieved her goal weight, I crested 300 pounds, and the parking lot rules changed at my job. I was now being directed to park just under a half-mile from my office. I became winded just walking to and from my car and office. I remember crying and praying in my parked car in the work lot about what to do. In the midst of this personal crisis, I felt guided to talk to my mom about it.

It was hard for me as a young, independent man to ask for help from anyone, let alone my mother. I confessed to Mom about those short, winded walks through the parking lot.

"These are supposed to be the healthiest years of my life and I have trouble just walking into my office building," I shared. "Mom, how did you do it? How did you lose the weight?"

She showed me an app, MyFitnessPal, talked to me about the importance of portion control, told me how I needed to find exercises that I actually enjoyed, and prayed for me. We talked and discussed the issues she had experienced herself, lending her advice in overcoming those areas. I came to realize that I was much more like my mother than I cared to admit. We shared a lot of the same vices: pizza, chips and, at the time, cigarettes (a nasty habit that I'd picked up in college). I committed to kicking all three of them to the curb.

At the time, it took a lot of pride swallowing to heed my mom's advice, but I was determined to feel healthy. She was not only my inspiration but also my motivator. *If my mom can do it, I can, too,* I told myself. I followed her footsteps. I utilized the motion tracking movement games that came with my video game console, like she had done with her dancing game that embarrassed my brother and I so much. I sat down and actually started reading the nutritional facts on all of my foods. I was most blown away by how portions are actually sized, a fact that Mom had warned me about. I began methodically scanning my foods and using the search function on MyFitnessPal to track meals. I slowly learned how to healthily cook for myself. I discovered that vegetables can be delicious, something the 10-year-old me would have never imagined. Weight would fall off for a while then I would plateau. I would seek Mom's counsel and she'd talk to me about how I should try to vary up my exercises . . . and she prayed with me.

I recalled how my friend Jon had lost weight by doing yoga in college but I was too self-conscious to attend a real yoga class. Bending over with my big butt in the air around a bunch of random people was something close to a nightmare for me. I also wasn't really interested in the spiritual side of yoga classes. Eventually, I found a series of yoga videos geared more towards breathing and body focus rather than an "inner peace." I began rotating through the videos every day after work in my apartment. I bought a pull-up bar at a yard sale and would make myself do a chin-up anytime I lost a video game match.

Whenever I'd find myself getting frustrated at my progress, I'd turn to my mother for advice. She always had some nugget of truth and a prayer for me. We bonded over our newly found healthy lifestyle, trading exercises and recipes, and rooting for one another's accomplishments. Eventually, I hit my personal goal: to be out of the obese BMI range. I had hit 195 pounds! I kept exercising and eating right but overall I thought I was done losing weight. Then Mom asked me something that I didn't want to hear.

I went and watched her and my dad compete in a mini-triathlon. Shortly after they crossed the finish line, she asked if I would join them the following year. I hated running and was still too self-conscious to go swimming. It seemed insurmountable to me, but in the back of my mind, *IF YOUR MOM CAN DO IT, SO CAN YOU* was screaming.

I hesitantly agreed. The fastest mile I'd ever run back in high school as part of the Presidential Fitness Test was 15 minutes, so I had a long way to go. I bought a pair of running shoes and began training once a week in lieu of one of my yoga routines. After a few months of wheezing my way through some city parks, I admitted to myself that I was neglecting kicking the one vice that was holding me back: smoking. I had tried to quit a couple of times but never really wanted to until then. That finish line was too close to stop now. Again, in the back of my mind was that voice: *If your mom can do it, so can you.* I crumpled the pack I'd had after coming home from an incredibly wheezy run and haven't picked up one since.

The following spring, I realized that I hadn't biked in seven years and should start training for that, as well. My dad passed down to me one of his old bikes and a helmet. I was set. Oddly enough, just like Mom, a flood of fun childhood memories came to me of being on a bike and I re-fell in love with this me-powered vehicle. I lived in the city of Pittsburgh and began utilizing the trails and safer bike routes through the city. I cycled the eight hilly miles to work, weather permitting. As a result, I dropped more pounds and finally entered the healthy weight range. I didn't think it was possible. I added going to adult swim at the community pool and doing laps on some weekends.

Alex before his weight loss and with his mom (Helen) at the finish line

That summer, Mom and I competed in the same mini-triathlon. I'll admit that it was challenging. My legs and arms felt like jelly climbing out of the water after the swim and I trudged up a hill to get on my bike, already feeling exhausted. My if-Mom-can-do-it mantra reverberated in my mind. Every hill my bike climb was powered by those words.

Cruising off the bike, I knew I was in the home stretch with just a 5k to go. At one point, Mom and I passed each other on the trail, cheering for one another as we passed. We both finished. I can't say I really enjoyed the triathlon but I am definitely glad I did it and I am even more glad that I ran it with my mom.

I am so thankful for the drive and support that Mom has given me on my weight loss journey. I couldn't have done it without her love, support and prayers. She and this book are proof that you cannot do this alone. It speaks to the power of having a good support system with family or friends, and especially God. Mom is an inspiration—to me and hopefully for you, too—because, "If my mom can do it, so can you."

—Alex Baratta

Life is not about the body, but our health is a means of praise. —Jimmy Pena

I was obese. There, I've said it.

It took me 46 years to admit this. Everyone could see my fat, but I hid from mirrors, cameras and anything that might have revealed the truth of my situation. I was far from Hollywood's ideal, ultrathin woman. Yet I rationalized: What is the harm of being the big woman, anyway? Who

Introduction

doesn't like a big paycheck, big car, big house, big-screen TV? In our modern world, bigger is better, right?

One day in 2004, I was flying to New York City for an important client visit, when I found myself unable to wriggle and squirm into the airplane seat. I thought it was some kind of trick on the part of the airline industry. Were they making the seats smaller? Did they shrink the size of the seatbelts? At a dress size 3X, the belt couldn't reach the clasp across my lap. Embarrassed, I asked the flight attendant to quietly slip me a seatbelt extender.

Up until this "get real" moment on the airplane, I had consistently fallen short and failed at the battle of the bulge. While I couldn't seem to regularly maintain a healthy weight, I had enjoyed many short-term successes. My weight chart looked like the Dow Jones: up, down, up, up, down, up, up, down and always back up no matter what I tried.

Finally, at the age of 35, no longer able to hide from myself that I was obese, I admitted ultimate defeat, gave up and moved onto other priorities

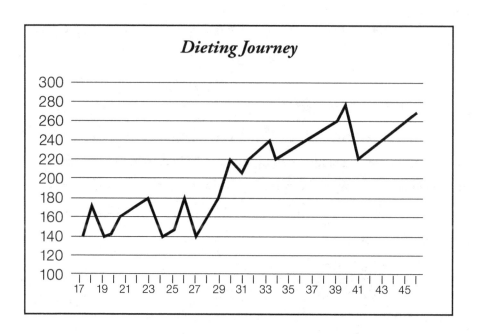

Dieting Journey

in life. Aside from this struggle, I had a lot to be thankful for, including a wonderful husband, Vince, who loves me just as I am, fat or thin. His career as a contract engineer had us relocating all over the country, and with each impending move, I lost weight then gained it back after we settled in a new location. It was fun to reinvent our lives with each relocation but this issue of being overweight followed me wherever we went. In spite of being loved and supported by Vince and other friends and family members, I felt powerless. Like so many others who struggle with weight, I tried everything: starvation in college, Weight Watchers before my wedding, diet pills after my first child, and Weight Watchers again after my second child when the scale tipped over 200 pounds.

I struggled with the disciplines of Weight Watchers. I felt dejected when I attended meetings in which my weight went up on the scale, not down. I would avoid the scale for weeks, only to be filled with dread then heartbroken when I finally stepped onto it and saw a number that I would swear would be the highest I'd ever weigh. I'd return to my medical doctor from time to time, but the drugs he prescribed worked only as long as I took them. (Yes, I am part of the Fen-Phen disaster.) I have lost 40 to 50 pounds so many times that, in total, I've probably dropped a staggering 450 pounds (the size of three people). I've honestly lost track. Each time, I'd get frustrated, quit and the weight would return with a few added pounds.

Eventually, I began to feel the physical effects of carrying extra weight. The more I ate, the more my lower body screamed in pain. My feet ached. My ankles and knees became enlarged and swollen. In response, I limited my physical activity to prevent the pain that was certain to follow. It became a vicious downward spiral. One day, thinking that I could have a little fun, I strained a leg muscle bowling duckpins with Vince and my sons. For weeks, I favored my left leg. Eventually, I could no longer walk.

The physical therapist discovered that my leg muscles had tightened in the wrong places and pulled my kneecap out of place. It took three months to strengthen my leg enough that I could walk without a limp. Physical therapy three times each week resulted in stronger muscles and a bonus weight loss. It was, of course, temporary. The pounds crept back on and, once again, my screaming knee pain got my attention. By now, since I'd been on this roller coaster for 30 years, I couldn't help but notice that every time I lost weight through diet and exercise, my "norm" was to gain back more. So I reasoned that I was better off doing nothing rather than repeatedly failing at this seemingly never-ending fight.

Clearly, something was missing and I was filling it with food. After three decades of struggle, I was convinced that there was no hope for me. I didn't understand back then that a lack of hope is a spiritual predicament, not an emotional or psychological one. I know now that for those who believe in Christ, He is the hope of the world, a higher power to whom those with faith turn for strength. The Bible verse "By myself I can do nothing" speaks to this. With Christ, everything is possible. But I wasn't a woman of faith in my younger adult years. I'd spent my twenties and thirties refusing to acknowledge God after I walked away from Him at age 14 when my parents divorced. I spent years trying to numb the fond memories of Sunday school, Bible camp and life with Jesus when I was a child and pre-teen. Even in my rebellion, the Lord continued to pursue me with relentless love. I wasn't yet ready to accept God's love, or even to love myself in a way that honors God.

In 1998, we moved to Pittsburgh, Pennsylvania, joined "Steelers Nation" and made new friends. One friend, Jane, invited me to church. I refused. Was I still mad at God about my parent's divorce? Could there be something at church that would fill the void I knew was there? Jane didn't give up. After two years and numerous invitations, I finally agreed to join her at church. It was an eye-opening experience, to say the least. During the service that day, I rediscovered the immense love that I felt as an 11-year-old girl in a Baptist church, where I first met and accepted Jesus. I realized what I had been missing: a relationship with Christ. I knew from my experiences with Jesus as a little girl that He loves everyone—even me—no matter our size, shape, state of mind, or what we have or have not done in our past.

I wish I could say that I immediately and effortlessly shed the weight without any problems or obstacles after that day in church, but that's not how my story plays out. I still had a "sizeable" amount of personal growth to do. I did have a vague sense that God had a plan for my life; however, I would come to learn that following His plan required listening and obedience—two of my weakest character traits.

* * *

I know now that being overweight is a physical problem with a spiritual solution. This book is about my journey, one step at a time, one pound at a time, as I learned to trust God. God accepted and loved me exactly as I was, yet cared for me and did not allow me to remain hopeless. My love for the Lord expanded as I learned to listen for and obey His promptings to get to the root of what was causing my weight issue. Every time that God helped me remove a scarred layer from my past, I embraced a new layer of trust in His plan for my life. I crawled then walked and finally ran free from a life of obesity to one of health and hope, which has given me the strength to accomplish the goals and dreams He had planned for my life.

At the beginning of each chapter, I use the analogy of restoring a wood floor because I feel the Lord did just that: He restored me as if I were a worn and marred floor covered with years of grime, nicks and built-up finish, sorely in disrepair. He removed the deep gouges in my heart and sanded one layer after another of my psyche so that I could find my courage. Along the way, He carefully and compassionately changed the sand paper from the hardest to the finest grit, paring down to the bare wood of my being. His handiwork removed decades of scars and lies that plagued me. These things

True Measure of Success

 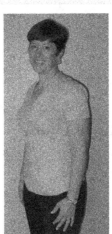

September 2006
271 pounds

July 2010
158 pounds

were the real culprit of my yo-yo weight gain and loss. As I faced all of this, so much of the old me was being slowly bundled up and carted away to a dumpster, never to return. Once the true beauty of my soul was revealed to me and polished up, I was able to finally reach and maintain a healthy weight. Praise God! I reached my goal in 2010 and each passing year since then has resulted in learning something new about myself, which adds even more luster to the Lord's protective finish.

I'm not going to mislead anyone by saying that my life became perfect and easy and wonderful. Just like everyone else, I've had my share of challenges but food is no longer my solution to coping with them.

In the chapters ahead, you will read about my struggles and successes. You'll read how others overcame challenges and shed their excess pounds and sustained their weight loss long term; their "True Measure of Success" stories are interspersed throughout the pages. At the end of each chapter, you'll be encouraged to "Apprentice with the Master Craftsman", taking time to reflect and identify new ideas and actions for your own wellness journey. Accompanying each chapter is suggested Scripture to include in your daily devotional time; these reinforce the theme of each chapter.

If you are reading this book with a friend or a small group, which I highly encourage, the Appendix includes a Small Group Discussion Guide to challenge, inspire and stretch you while growing closer to God. I repeat the daily Scripture devotions from the end of each chapter for easy reference. My hope is that these exercises will jump-start your transformation even before you finish the book. To further send you on your way, I have included in the Appendix a handful of diet programs for you to research during your weight loss and maintenance journey.

* * *

Have you tried everything else? Are you working someone else's plan or your own plan? Or maybe, like me, you've given up and "no plan" is your plan. I wrote about my journey to help others understand that there certainly is a "plan" for your life—God's plan.

Jeremiah 29:11 says: "For I know the plans I have for you, declares the Lord, plans to prosper you and not to harm you, plans to give you hope and a future." Will you dare to let God be all He says He will be in your life?

When we believe God can do a miracle in our lives, He does a miracle. Will you believe? Get set for perhaps the most transformational journey of your life—your path back to health and a deeper reliance on God.

Part One

Assess, Prep and Clean
the Surface

Prep Work

Pray diligently. Stay alert, with your eyes wide open in gratitude.
(Colossians 4:2)

Floor refinishing is a highly skilled occupation. How do I know this? I watched my grandfather build and restore homes. I learned from him that anyone with a sander can say they're in the business of flooring. Yet only a true master craftsman can restore the beauty of wood beneath its marred finish.

*

When Grandpa died at age 95, he was still overseeing a crew and renovating houses. My grandmother lived to be 98. Both of their mothers (my great-grandmothers) lived to be 99. With those genes, I might live to be a centenarian or at least have a long life, barring any unforeseen fatal accident, injury or illness. Yet it's about the quality of those years, not how many we are given. I want to live independently and enjoy life for as long as possible, just like my grandparents. I know that caring for my body now will reap rewards in the future. Yet knowing and doing are two different things.

I grew up in what seemed like a normal home in Arnold, Maryland, near Annapolis. My mom stayed home raising three girls who were born by the time she was 22. She was our scout leader, children's church leader, community leader, and kept our house running. All in a day's work, she replaced the plug on the vacuum, fixed the leaky faucet, sewed our matching outfits for school, and swatted us on the bottom when we didn't obey. She worked hard to make ends meet.

In summertime, my sisters and I swam, rode bikes and explored the neighborhood. Monday through Friday, we played all day and only came home for lunch and dinner. Saturday mornings, we'd race through our chores so we could get outside to play. In 1967, when I was in second grade, Mom went to night school. The following year when my youngest sister, Cyndi, entered kindergarten, Mom went to work loading key punch cards into newfangled types of machines called "computers."

Me [left] and my sisters,
Cyndi and Kathy, in 1967

My dad worked as a salesman Monday through Saturday. He left for work at 10 in the morning and returned after we were asleep. When Dad was home, life was a party. Since we rarely saw him, it was fun and exciting when we were with him. Yet those parties abruptly ended once we were all tucked into bed. I spent many sleepless nights listening to my parent's verbal wars as they lashed out at each other. Most of the time, they fought about money or the lack of it. I worried about what might happen to us without enough money. I comforted myself by clinging to my blanket, the edge eventually worn bare from years of nervously rubbing the satin binding between my fingers.

Church became a place of refuge. Smiling faces welcomed us to Sunday school each week. The building had a sense of peace that I felt each time I walked in the door. The Wednesday night pot luck dinners were the highlight of the week. Where else could we get deviled eggs and macaroni and cheese? I distinctly remember having my first stuffed cabbage, chocolate éclair and pretzel Jell-O dessert at those gatherings—all things that Mom didn't serve at home.

In the summer of 1971, I spent a week at Camp Wo-Me-To in northeastern Maryland, where I met Jesus for the first time. Shortly after camp, I went forward at church and invited Jesus into my heart. I still remember the joy I experienced when I emerged from the water during my baptism. I loved Jesus and shared my testimony with anyone who would listen.

Life Takes a Turn

Three years later, life took a tumultuous turn. My parent's arguments continued day and night. One time, my parents sent my sisters and me out of the house so they could scream in private. The three of us leaned on each other like a tripod, emotionally holding each other up. As we sat in the front yard, voices bellowed from the house for everyone in the neighborhood to hear. The leaves on the trees rustled together, as if sharing in our shuddering. A few weeks later, Mom broke the news: "Your dad and I are getting a divorce." I popped off a snide remark: "It's about time."

Christmas of 1974 was a dark day in our house. Dad was to move out the next day. Our parents screamed at each other, with Mom finally pleading, "Can't we get along? It's our last Christmas!" My stomach was turning over as we sat together at dinner, pretending to have a merry Christmas.

Cyndi, who had just turned 11 in November, curled up on the couch in a fetal position and stared into space. We all knew that the bill collector had been calling the week prior. Perhaps they might repossess Christmas, as well? Years later as an adult, I realized that the depression I feel every Christmas is directly related to this day in our family's history.

The following day after that Christmas in 1974, with my sisters' and my fears now coming to fruition, we helped Dad move. We met Jene when we arrived at his new one-bedroom apartment. He introduced her as the "love of his life" and said they planned to marry as soon as both of their divorces were final. No wonder my dad was never at home! He was now starting a new life with a "new wife" and this tiny space appeared to be only for them, as there wasn't even enough room for all of us to sit down and eat. This was clearly not a place where we would spend much time. I felt like Dad was divorcing me, too. I forced a smile and dreaded what life would be like with a stepmother.

From then on, instead of church on Sunday, we spent mandatory time with our "new" family, which now consisted of my two sisters (then ages 13 and 11), myself (14), my future two stepbrothers (16 and 18), Dad (then 34) and Jene (41). Since there was no room for us to hang out at their new apartment, we'd cram into Jene's Mercury Marquis—three in the front and four in the back—and they'd take us on long drives to places that Jene wanted to see. My Sundays went from being a day of comfort and fellowship to a fake day, when everyone smiled and acted like all was well and that life was good, whether we felt that way or not.

Months later, my parents sold our family home as part of the divorce settlement. We moved with Mom to a smaller house in Glen Burnie, Maryland, near where she worked. At 33, Mom was now single for the first time since she was 18. She enjoyed her freedom, often meeting friends after work for drinks and dancing. As time went on, she came home later and later each night. Eventually, we only saw her in the mornings when she'd return home from a night with her new boyfriend. She'd check on us, shower, dress and head off to work again.

I took on the bossy big sister role. Kathy and Cyndi would be happy to confirm that I ruled the roost. We packed our lunches, cooked our dinners and helped each other with our homework. We calmed each other's fears when something went bump in the night. We clung together, wondering what would happen next.

Without supervision, I started hanging out with a rough group who smoked cigarettes and marijuana, and broke into cars to pay for their nasty habits. Once holding up a purse that they'd snatched from an unlocked car in a church parking lot, my friends laughed and said, "Those fools at church think God is watching their cars." To this day, I lock my car, no exception. Evil is everywhere, even in church parking lots.

During this dark season of my life, I began an unhealthy journey that took decades to reverse. I joined in the smoking with my friends, purposely hoping my actions would upset my mom. I knew I was changing into someone I didn't want to become. I felt lost and inwardly worried about my future. Everything came to a head when Mom handed me money one day and asked me to stop at the grocery store after school. I walked past the store on my mile walk to high school each day. Apparently, she didn't have time to bring food back home after work and we didn't have food in the house for dinner. Something snapped in me that day. I was done. I no longer wanted this responsibility of caretaking my siblings thrust upon me as it was.

The following Sunday during our weekly visitation with Dad, I broke down and shared my frustration. (I still wonder what would have happened if I'd shared my frustration with Mom instead?) Next, nothing short of a world war broke out between my parents. First, Dad and Jene hashed out (loud enough for all of us to hear) how us coming to live with them would change their future plans. My dad focused on dollar signs. If we lived with him, he wouldn't have to pay child support, so they could afford a larger house.

Once Jene agreed that we could come live with them, another big blow-up transpired between my parents. My sisters were forced to choose between Mom and Dad. Cyndi came with me to Dad's. Kathy (always closer to Mom) stayed behind. Each week, we'd hug Kathy when she arrived for Sunday visitations. As sisters, we understood that Kathy needed to support Mom, as they'd always shared a close bond. Only a few months later, Kathy asked to join us when Mom's boyfriend moved in with them.

The next few months were filled with disruption, uncertainty and a renewed sense of abandonment. In the short time since Dad married Jene, her ex-husband passed away, forcing us to move into the home where my two stepbrothers had lived most of their lives. The situation was beyond awkward with all of us living in the same house. They were grieving the loss of their dad and now had to share their house with their stepfather, who moved into the master bedroom with their mom and three stepsisters sleeping on the lower level family room. They had never had sisters and we'd never had brothers. We averted our eyes the first morning they walked into the kitchen in their underwear.

That house never felt like our home. Jene was very strict on what food we could eat. Her sons could snack—after all, this was their house. But anytime my sisters or I ate something from the pantry, we would be screamed at for doing so. "Who ate the chips?" "Who drank the milk?" "Why is the peanut butter gone?" Us girls were expected to buy our own toiletries and feminine hygiene products with our baby-sitting money, whereas the stepbrothers got whatever they wanted or needed. Life was hell.

By the end of that school year, our house was sold and we moved to another school district. Dad and Jene bought a four-bedroom townhouse in Laurel, Maryland, near where they both worked. Since my stepbrothers were older, they got the two smaller rooms. My sisters and I shared a room. At least I got a single bed; Kathy and Cyndi shared bunk beds. The walk-in closet overflowed with clothes for three teenage girls. I turned 16 that summer and started working at a local fast food chain. Kathy soon joined me at work. With both of us working, at least now we had a supply of food coming into the house that we could eat without feeling like criminals. I see now how this circumstance set me up for deep-rooted future issues with food.

Cracks in the Foundation

In the three years following the divorce, I lived in four houses and attended three high schools. Out of self-preservation, I created tunnel vision for myself. In times of despair, I'd find a quiet place and remind myself that others had worse situations. At least I had a roof over my head and food to eat. I relied on myself and no one else—least of all, God. I no longer read *The Living Bible* Mom had given me when I was 13, before this mess started. I no longer attended church and ended up isolated in my thoughts without my Christian mentors to help me understand that bad things happen to everyone. I blamed God and decided that I was better off on my own.

My dad's lifestyle opened up a world of new challenges. In his house, drinking and smoking marijuana were acceptable—not only for him, Jene and their friends, but also for me, my siblings and our friends. From Dad's perspective, we were responsible with our alcohol and drug use as long as we could fulfill our responsibilities outside the house. My friends thought it was great. We had the cool parents. I was a National Honor Society student, worked at my job after school to save money for college, and spent most of my free time numb to the world as a closet drug user.

Once I got to college, I had a harder time functioning at the higher level that was expected of me during those years. I struggled to maintain a healthy balance of working my way through college and maintaining an enviable party life. Once I met my sweet husband, Vince, that all changed. Finishing my studies so that I could be with him became more important than partying. He put me on a new path and literally saved my life. Vince was never a fan of cigarettes, so after 10 years of smoking and five years of us dating, I had my last cigarette on our wedding day in 1984.

I cleaned up my act and began a blessed life with a wonderful husband and, within a few years, our two sons. By then I had graduated and had begun a successful career working in the field of health insurance. Unfortunately, something else had become my drug of choice: food. My weight steadily increased as I coped with life by using food. I tipped the scales at 200 during my second pregnancy and that was only the beginning.

Even though I'd taken a faith detour, the Lord never gave up on me. He was always reminding me of His presence. In college, I'd attended church with several different friends when I went home with them over the weekends. When I met Vince, his mother was my example of what it looked like to follow Christ. I knew she'd prayed for us. I am ever so thankful that she encouraged us to get married in her church.

Vince and I lived in seven states during the first 20 years of our relationship. As I mentioned earlier, every time we moved, I would make new friends who would invite me to join them at church. I always politely said, "No, thank you." My friends never made me feel guilty. To the contrary, I was the one who felt uncomfortable knowing that I was willfully ignoring God.

Deep down inside, I felt that my children needed to know the Lord. I wasn't ready to attend church, so I sent them to day cares and preschools at churches. In fact, when we moved to Pittsburgh in 1998, my son Davis met his best friends, two brothers, at a church after-school day care. Their mom, Jane, was the friend who never stopped inviting me to church. Jane was different. She asked how she could pray for me. She read her Bible and shared the insights she received with me. She attended a small group with others from her church. Jane and her group spent two years praying for me before I finally walked into church. Finally, my "no" turned into a "yes" when I gave my life back to Christ in 2000.

* * *

I am pleased to share the first success story of the book by giving voice to Shannon Greenleaf, whom I met at church. When I learned that she, too, was a blessed "big loser", I asked her to share her journey. She and I have walked similar yet different paths.

True Measure of Success: Shannon Greenleaf

Before and after

Although I did not realize it, the reinvention of my life started on my darkest day, July 14, 2009, at the age of 36, the day I lost my father to complications of diabetes and obesity. His death shocked me since I'd planned on bringing him home from the hospital the following day. I organized my father's final arrangements since my mom was barely able to function. My young daughter fell into a deep depression, devastated by the loss of her grandfather.

Over the next two years, my life spiraled out of control. I contracted Swine flu and also experienced paralysis and weakness from Bell's Palsy. With my health at an all-time low, my doctor cautioned me about my weight. I controlled my borderline diabetes and high blood pressure with medication. Overweight my entire life, each time I tried to lose, I'd experience some success, then gained it back along with more weight than I lost.

In 2011, when I realized I wouldn't live past 40 if I didn't to do something to get my health under control, I walked into Weight Watchers. My weight stunned me: 250 pounds. I stood five feet, one-inch-and-a-half tall. I was morbidly obese. I left my first meeting ready to change. The plan clicked with me. Eating became a game of numbers. I learned how to eat healthy by understanding what to eat and the concept of portion control.

At times, the journey seemed impossible and emotionally draining. I went from a couch potato to never sitting still, from not exercising to walking a little every day. As I changed the way I ate and moved my body, I consistently lost weight, finally reaching my goal on February 3, 2012. I've maintained my 137 pounds within five pounds for more than four years.

I joined the Weight Watchers leadership team, which helps me stay on track and holds me accountable. Yet, losing weight was only the beginning of my health journey. I needed to endure the psychological and emotional aspects as I learned control.

Although happy because I achieved my goal, I still saw myself as the 250-pound woman. I grabbed size 24 clothing when in actuality I wore a size six. When I looked in the mirror I didn't see the new me; my mind remembered the old me. I still wrestle with this issue today. When people compliment me, I have a difficult time believing that they are sincere. I am my own worst critic and needed to learn self-love. As time passes, I am better than I was when I first reached my goal. Yet, sometimes my mind's eye sees the old me before my journey started.

I believe I began to love myself when I accepted Jesus Christ as Lord and Savior. If He can love me the way I am, who am I to think poorly of myself? Now, when I start to doubt myself or struggle with my thoughts and issues, I turn to God. I look at my body now as a vessel that God can use to help others. I want to remain healthy to do the good works that He has put in front of me. When I am having a hard time staying on track, I turn to 1 Corinthians 6:19-20:

"Do you not know that your bodies are temples of the Holy Spirit, who is in you, whom you have received from God? You are not your own; you were bought at a price.

Therefore, honor God with your bodies."

When I stumble into a funk and am dealing with negative thoughts about myself, I remind myself that I am not honoring God. When I am struggle, I ask for God to give me the eyes to see myself as He sees me. God is now directing my life and I believe that He will use the hurts and struggles I have overcome to help others. God gave his Son's life for my life. My life is too precious to waste it by letting negative self-talk creep into my brain. Not every day is easy, but with God walking beside me, it is possible.

Shannon continues to persevere on her wellness journey. As you read the various success stories throughout the book, I hope you will draw inspiration from their experiences and are encouraged on your own journey.

Making Up for Lost Time

In 2000, when I walked into church, I'd been away from the Lord for 26 years. I had a lot of making up to do. I became a super servant. You name it, I tried it. The children's ministry wasn't really for me. I found my niche in the tech ministry. Each week, I created the slides projected during the weekend services.

Jane insisted I join a small group. I wish I could say I was no longer in rebellion. The honest answer is that I dragged my feet. I had the instinct that something was going to happen to me in that small group. I was going to change.

Jane's persistence finally paid off when I joined a group that formed out of a church membership class I'd attended. As I suspected, small group stretched me spiritually. I saw people learning how to live out their faith. I timidly learned to pray aloud, for one person then by opening and leading the group in prayer. I was encouraged by those who were further ahead of me spiritually. We served together at a local personal care home, providing food and playing games with residents who longed for interaction with others.

I wanted to change how I lived my life but had no clue how to begin. My small group leader, Mark Belko, suggested prayer. I asked the Lord how to change my schedule so that I could work in daily time with Him. I asked Him to help me understand what I was reading. I bought a study Bible in order to research the background of what I was reading. I enrolled in classes offered at church to better understand the New and Old Testaments. Over time, I developed confidence in what I was reading. I learned that <u>instead of giving God a slice of my life, He wanted me to place Him in the center</u>. Within a year, I apprenticed in preparation to lead my own small group. As you read this, it may sound like I was humming along, but looking back, my relationship with God was still superficial. I still had a lot of work ahead of me.

* * *

As I've come to personally learn, restoration requires work and can be quite difficult at times. We need to reflect on new ways of thinking and always prepare ourselves for the next steps in our own wellness journey. I encourage you to spend time alone with the Lord, the ultimate Master Craftsman. Before turning to the next chapter, take time to respond to the following prompts.

Apprentice with the Master Craftsman

God never gave up on me. He wanted to have a relationship with me, just as He wants to have a relationship with each of us. God continues even today to astound me. He loves each of us and knows everything about us. Yet it is up to us to respond. I am sorry that it took me so long.

You might be surprised by what your inner self might want to say to God. If you were like me, you might find it hard to make time and space to quietly sit before the Lord. I invite you to sit quietly for the sole purpose of allowing yourself to listen to the quiet voice within. What might you want to say to God? Even more importantly, what might God want to say to you? What is God revealing to you that you find difficult to accept? Take time now to sit with these questions.

Prayer:

Lord, you know where I am, what I've done, who I've become, and how I feel. Search me, O God, and know my heart; test me and know my anxious thought. See if there is any offensive way in me, and lead me in the way everlasting. (Psalm 139:23-24).

You can receive Christ or recommit your life to Christ through the following prayer.

Lord Jesus, I need You. Thank You for dying on the cross for my sins. I open myself to You and receive You as my Savior and my Lord. Thank You for forgiving my sins and giving me eternal life. Teach me how to give you first place in my life. Amen.

Devotions:

Romans 3 - Faith and Righteousness

John 1:1-18 – In the Beginning

Romans 5 - Life Through Christ

John 10:1-21 - The Good Shepherd and His Sheep

Romans 6 - Alive in Christ

2.
Are You Ready Yet?

Yesterday is gone. Tomorrow has not yet come. We have only today.
Let us begin.

--Mother Teresa

I peered down at the wood floor in my living room and wondered how many times the chairs had been moved back and forth, scraping grooves into it. Deeply embedded dirt within each crevice emphasized the scars, black against the wood's natural golden hue. Sunlight only illuminates the scratched lines that intersected haphazardly on the dulled floor. I considered the disruption that a restoration project would cause in my life. I wondered if I was ready.

*

About two years after returning to the church, I'd heard about our church's "Encounter with God" retreat and sensed that the Lord wanted me to attend. I hesitated, wondering what God might ask of me. Again, Jane came to the rescue. She was attending and insisted that I attend with her. Where would we be without others encouraging us on our faith journey?

My Encounter with God

In 2002, I attended the "Encounter with God" retreat and began in earnest to inspect the situations and actions of my past. That week, I discovered the various barriers that I had created to protect myself. Unfortunately—or, perhaps fortunately—these same barriers were obstructing my relationship with God, so eradicating them would mean a new freedom that I had no idea existed.

During the retreat, I inventoried my life. In doing so, I had two valuable realizations. First, memories of drug and alcohol abuse within my birth family bounced back into the forefront of my thoughts. I loathed my dad's lifestyle, which was still continuing for him. Now age 62, he smoked five packs of cigarettes a day, as well as the occasional joint. He consumed a constant flow of bourbon into what had now become a ravaged body. I was ashamed and embarrassed by my dad.

Unspoken hurts I'd never considered came forward as I recounted my life with Dad. I'd strived to reach his expectations and earn his admiration. My "A" and "B" grades never measured up. Straight "A's" were the only acceptable standard, which I strived for but never achieved. He happened to be working the night that I was inducted into the National Honor Society, so I never got my moment to shine in his presence.

Another area in which I didn't meet Dad's standards was my appearance. My hair was never blonde enough, my body shape never thin enough, my gait and poise never graceful enough. In my childhood, he'd once told me after a playground mishap that I would never find a husband because I had too many scars on my legs. It's funny how those words still sting.

Even during my wedding, Dad's words left an emotional mark. Six months before my big day in 1984, I joined Weight Watchers and worked diligently to lose weight. I dropped 40 pounds, reached my goal and maintained my healthy weight. After six weeks at goal, Weight Watchers awarded me with their "lifetime" Weight Watchers designation. (Tucked away in my dresser drawer is the large gold key I'd received to recognize my accomplishment.) Of course, I wanted to look my best on my wedding day. I weighed 142 pounds and wore a size 10 wedding dress. I was feeling pretty good about all of this until the wedding rehearsal. Dad's penetrating words are still cemented in my memory:

"I'm surprised your thighs look so thick after all the weight you've lost." That was my father's idea of a compliment, I guess.

Onlookers of my life might say that I've had great success in my career, my marriage, as a mother, daughter and sister. Yet, my dad withholding his praise and affection still caused me to feel like I could never measure up, particularly to his vision for me. My father's disappointment enraged me in 1990 when I decided to put a hold on my management career in the health insurance industry and become a stay-at-home mom after the birth of my second son, Davis.

"Why would anyone want to stay home and be a mom?" my father asked during a phone conversation.

I hung up, determined to distance myself from him and live my life on my own terms. I felt the need to insulate my sons from their grandfather. I didn't want them exposed to his negative outlook, the drugs, alcohol and his newest vice, gambling.

All of this came back into my memory as I attended that retreat in 2002. I was once and for all ready to face this hard truth that had affected me so deeply, causing me to relate to God the Heavenly Father through the painful relationship with my earthy father.

My "2 x 4" Moment

In much the same way that I removed myself from my father's life for over a decade, I spent 24 years resisting a relationship with God. During the 2002 retreat, I was able to uncover the truth about the love and forgiveness He provides. I experienced what I call a "2 x 4 moment" when I recognized that, unlike my dad, God was perfect and loved me as a Heavenly Father. The more I embraced God's love, the more my bitterness towards my dad dissolved. Inside I shouted, "Yahoo! Hallelujah! God loves me no matter what." Immediately, joy filled my life as the burden lifted.

With the initial layers of filth and grime removed, I began to view Dad through Jesus' eyes. I saw a hurt person numbing himself with alcohol and drugs. Upon returning home from the retreat, I telephoned my father, inspired by my renewed faith and cautiously hopeful for a better relationship. Thankfully, I learned at the retreat how to set healthy boundaries for myself. Gradually, Dad and I began spending time each week talking on the telephone. Even when his hurtful words continued, my new perspective helped me to immediately forgive him and move on. Dad recognized this difference in my approach towards him, which eventually led to deeper discussions about Jesus. Dad welcomed my willingness to spend more time with him. I intentionally continued to telephone him every other week or so to check in and talk with him.

Once I refocused on God's love and forgiveness, I realized that I needed to forgive in other areas of my life. I'd blamed God and others for my wrongful actions and negative thoughts, as well as the hurtful actions of others. I thought I'd already forgiven my mom; however, I made sure to release any residual bitterness. I even forgave God. He didn't need my forgiveness. It was me who needed to release the bitterness that unforgiveness harbors. Finally, I forgave myself for the years I'd missed out on my relationship with God. I experienced peace, joy and thankfulness.

I returned multiple times over the next 10 years to that "Encounter with

God" retreat. Each time, I discovered a new deeply embedded scratch or scar about myself, another truth that needed to be "buffed out." One time, I released my need to perform for God. At another retreat, I recognized I was not an accident and my days were ordained in his book (Psalm 139). I also came to learn that God had a purpose for my life, greater than anything I could imagine.

Pursuing My Purpose

My spiritual life continued to deepen with every retreat, yet I still resisted any prompting that I needed to take better care of myself. I attended every leadership training course offered by my church and looked for other ways to grow spiritually. In 2004, I stumbled across the book *The Purpose Driven Life: What on Earth Am I Here For?* by Rick Warren. Chapter one ended with a question: "In spite of all the advertising around me, how can I remind myself that life is really about living for God and not myself?" I jammed the book back onto the shelf, pondering, *What do you mean it's not about me?*

No doubt, our relentlessly loving Father has a great sense of humor. Months after I gave up on that book, our church sponsored a campaign called "The Purpose Driven Life: What on Earth Am I Here For?" As a small group leader, I was required to read and discuss this very book, which the campaign was based upon. So, I retrieved it from my bookshelf and each day, I read and answered the questions. Challenged to lead by example, I dug deeper into my life purpose and the barriers that I needed help to remove. Here are a few of my daily responses:

> Day Four: "Since I was made to last forever, what is the one thing I should stop doing and the one thing I should start doing today?" Answer: Gaining and losing weight.

Day 10: "What area of my life am I holding back from God?" Answer: My weight issues.

Day 24: "What has God already told me in his Word that I haven't started doing yet?" Answer: Maintaining a healthy body.

Day 35: "Am I limiting God's purpose in my life by trying to hide my weakness? What do I need to be honest about in order to help others? Answer: My weight.

Notice any common denominators? Well, even though I wanted to live out the purpose for my life, although I remained clueless of it, my passion to serve could not outweigh (no pun intended) my body's inability to move without pain. No amount of medication relieved the chronic pain in my feet, knees and hips due to my excess weight. I was stuck!

But it wasn't my physical self that was holding me back; it was my attitude. I refused to act on what I knew was important to fulfilling my purpose. The years of weight-loss failures looped in my mind like a bad pop song. I'd spent decades coping with life by stuffing myself with food. That full feeling in my stomach was my soul mate. Instead of fuel for my body, food was an intimate companion. The lie now deeply embedded, I weighed in at 274 pounds and identified myself as forever obese, so losing weight and helping others couldn't possibly be my purpose.

A few months after finishing *The Purpose Driven Life* with my small group, I faced another reminder of about weight loss. Cyndi told me about a Christian weight loss program called "First Place 4 Health" (FP4H). She suggested that I start a FP4H group at my church.

Had my sister lost her mind? I flat out told her, "No, I'm not interested."

My internal battle raged as I found every excuse to not pursue this idea.

"No, I don't want to."

"No, I don't have time."

"No, I've failed at weight loss."

"No, there is no hope for me when it comes to weight loss."

Even though I had accepted Jesus, I never considered that He would be interested in my weight. I'd gotten myself into this dilemma. I was the one overfeeding my body. "No" was my first response. So I got curious: Why was it that I followed the rules everywhere else in life, yet when it came to my health, I consistently said no?

After that visit with my sister, whenever I sensed a prompting in my consciousness about starting that weight loss program, it was as if I'd put my fingers in my ears and hummed, "La, La, La, La, La, La, La!" to drown out the Lord. I did not want to hear it. This had its consequences. The longer I refused to listen, the less I sensed God during my devotion time. I went from having wonderful, spirit-filled quiet time every day to complete silence.

Weeks turned into months. My resistance went on for so long that I forgot why I was rebelling. I had sensed His presence in my life vibrantly for five years since I'd recommitted to Christ, and now I did not sense God at all. I've heard this referred to as spiritual winter or dryness (something I hope to never experience again.) After many months of this dry spell, I felt lonely. Out of frustration, I searched for study guides and books to ignite my devotional time. One day, a question from my devotion asked:

"What is God asking you to do today that you are not willing to do?" It was a question similar to what I had written about in my small group study of Rick Warren's book. For the first time in over a year, I sensed that God wanted me to start a weight loss group at my church. It felt as if lightning bolts came down from heaven and shot through my heart as I sat in my chair. I was finally ready to say "yes" and surrender my big fat problem to the Lord—this time, in front of other people who were feeling vulnerable, as well.

Too afraid that I would back out, I immediately emailed my pastors. They immediately approved the start of the weight loss ministry. The pace was almost too fast and my doubt crept in.

Was I really supposed to start this group?

Why would anyone come to a weight loss program led by an obese woman?

Who am I to think I could lead this group?

There is no hope for me! I've lost and gained, lost and gained, lost and gained, again and again.

I wanted to jump off this roller coaster so badly. Instead, I stopped in my tracks, retreated to safety and did what anyone in my shaky condition would do: I did nothing—for months.

One summer day in 2006, after about four months of stalling, the Lord sent RJ, my small group pastor.

"What happened to the weight loss program?" she asked.

Honestly, I did not know what to say. Do I share my fear? Do I admit that I am dragging my feet? The question was exactly the encouragement I needed. I heard myself answer her question:

"...Oh, I am going to start it in September."

Holy cow, I made a specific commitment! I'd better get started.

That week, I ordered the Group Starter Kit from the First Place 4 Health website. I read everything and followed the instructions word for word. I was thankful for the step-by-step details. I publicized the program in the church bulletin, and put an advertisement in the local newspaper and neighborhood magazine. I asked friends, family and anyone I could find to pray about the program.

Soon enough, September arrived and I held my first orientation. I prayed that God would send at least three people; He sent 23. I was amazed! After that orientation, people repeatedly thanked me for starting the program, and many shared how they had been praying for months to have a Christ-centered health plan. Was it possible that my actions served as the answer to others' prayers? I felt so . . . well, purposeful! I wondered why it had taken me so long to say yes to this opportunity.

Learning How to "ACT"

I was experiencing the truth that God restores us when we place our hope in Him and take steps towards victory. We may stumble, yet He will not allow us to fall. He upholds us with his hand (Psalm 37:23-24). We have the opportunity to jump off the emotional eating merry-go-round as soon as our desperate cries reach His ears; he surrounds us with unconditional love and mercy.

Here is the first part of what I learned to do when you are not sure where to begin. We must be willing to take a risk. A truly sacred weight loss journey starts by "ACT-ing" on these steps:

A = Admit your weakness. Until we recognize our need, we are disabled and powerless. Set aside time alone with God. Open your conversation with God repeating the following Bible verses:

"Come to Me, all who are weary and heavy-laden, and I will give you rest. Take my yoke upon you and learn from me, for I am gentle and humble in heart, and you will find rest for your souls. For my yoke is easy and my burden is light." (Matthew 11:28-30)

"Straightening up, Jesus said to her, 'Woman, where are they? Did no one condemn you?' She said, 'No one, Lord.' And Jesus said, 'I do not condemn you, either. Go. From now on sin no more'." (John 8:10-11)

"And He has said to me, 'My grace is sufficient for you, for power is perfected in weakness.' Most gladly, therefore, I will rather boast about my weaknesses, so that the power of Christ may dwell in me." (2 Corinthians 12:9)

"For we do not have a high priest who cannot sympathize with our weaknesses, but One who has been tempted in all things as we are, yet without sin. Therefore, let us draw near with confidence to the throne of grace, so that we may receive mercy and find grace to help in time of need." (Hebrews 4:15-16)

"The weapons we fight with are not the weapons of the world. On the contrary, they have divine power to demolish strongholds." (2 Corinthians 10:4)

As you quiet yourself, listen for God's prompting to the following questions.

- What opinions and culture dictate my eating habits?

- How am I hurting myself with food in a quest for comfort?

- What foods and desires have I elevated above my relationship with God?

C = Claim God's truth. Recognize the Lord's direction, command or request and acknowledge His authority over your life. When we admit that we are not in control, we see a more genuine truth versus an it's-all-about-me self-centeredness. When we release our agenda, we open the door to His strength and plan for our lives. Jesus says, "Whoever wants to be my disciple must deny themselves and take up their cross and follow me." (Mark 8:34)

Confessing the authority of Jesus releases God's power so the fruits of the Spirit are present in our lives. "But the fruit of the Spirit is love, joy, peace, forbearance, kindness, goodness, faithfulness, gentleness and self-control. Against such things there is no law." (Galatians 5:22-23)

I needed self-control and it is last in the list of the fruits of the Spirit. God's power comes with spiritual discipline. I love Paul's letter to the Galatians. He identifies our selfish desires and God's provision for us through the Holy Spirit. The *Message* version of Galatians 5:16-18 reads: "My counsel is this: Live freely, animated and motivated by God's Spirit. Then you won't feed the compulsions of selfishness. For there is a root of sinful self-interest in us that is at odds with a free spirit, just as the free spirit is incompatible with selfishness. These two ways of life are antithetical, so that you cannot live at times one way and at times another way according to how you feel on any given day. Why don't you choose to be led by the Spirit and so escape the erratic compulsions of a law-dominated existence?"

When we identify the false thoughts and recognize our weaknesses, we acknowledge and receive His power as we call out to Him. For some, including me, fight a lasting battle against our weaknesses. Forever freedom requires continual reliance and faith in God's supernatural power.

T = Tell: Once we admit our weaknesses and claim God's truth, we must tell others. Overcoming emotional eating requires a team effort. We humble ourselves when we include others in our personal struggle. I am thankful for the support I received (and continue to receive) from my accountability group. They help me to remember that my body is the temple of the Holy Spirit and my wellness efforts result from my desire to serve God. Countless times before, I'd given up. I'd given up and run from the scale. I'd given up and regained the weight. I'd given up and added another failed attempt at wellness. I'd given up and no longer wanted anyone to know the truth on the scale. Ironically, everyone else could see my burgeoning body.

Now that I am at my goal weight (the rest of the chapters reveal how I achieved this), I speak with someone each week about my weakness. I admit that I still need the help of my group to keep me honest. I need someone to look at the scale. I am thankful for their praise when I have success and desperate for their encouragement when I am struggling. I have learned through this group process that we need not travel this wellness journey alone.

You may be reading this and observe that the success stories in this book mean that we've figured it all out. Most are surprised to experience that the battle continues. Regardless of the weight lost—20, 40, 80, 160 or over 200 pounds—many persist in the fight. When we have fought alongside others with a common enemy and relied on the Holy Spirit to fight our battles, we spend time thanking God for the miracles and continue asking for more. We celebrate and cheer each other on for all the striving and surviving while we wage on towards wellness.

True Measure of Success: Shanda Thornsberry

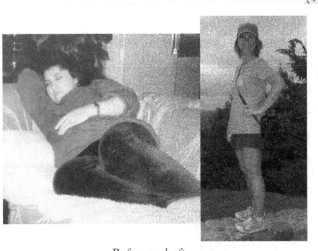

Before and after

I met the Shanda Thornsberry at the FP4H Summit in Houston, Texas in 2014. I asked her to share in her own words how admitting her weakness started her on the journey to success.

I was in bondage to food, addicted to sugar and had dieted since the age of 14. I have a family history of obesity, diabetes, heart disease, high blood pressure and cholesterol. Through God's mercy, I escaped other addictions, but the food one would be big enough.

Young, single and on my own, I lived on fast food, chocolate and sweets. I carried the same habits into my marriage and packed on 25 pounds immediately. One morning, determined to find something sweet in the kitchen,

I had nothing but brown sugar in the pantry. One or two spoonsful of brown sugar did not satisfy my craving. I went back every 15 minutes or so until the entire package was gone. I attacked it with the same vengeance that an addict hunts down alcohol or drugs. Afterwards, I sat on the couch and had one of the biggest cries of my life, telling the Lord my sorrow and repentance. I talked with my husband and let him know the truth. I began a new surrender to God.

Looking back, I see that I'd surrendered to the Lord, accepted the free gift of salvation, and sincerely repented. Still, I had no idea about the power available to me through the Holy Spirit. Enter FP4H, where I began to learn and continue to learn, session after session, year after year, how to recognize Jesus as my Lord and authority in the process of surrender and obedience. Through my learning process, I would test out that obedience— kicking, screaming, complaining, and digging my heels in—only to find out that God was faithful to me. He equips me, fulfills me, satisfies me, soothes me, comforts me, shows me balance, and empowers me with His Word.

I'm hooked, and I want to keep living this way. I have traded my food addiction for the best craving of all; the one we are created for: addicted to the One and Only. Unspeakable joy accompanies obedience. God allowed me to break a legacy of poor health and escape the bondage of food addiction. With God, I keep learning new things as we navigate the challenges of my weight maintenance plan together. My choice is to walk in freedom in God's strength.

Since 2010, Shanda has continued to maintain her healthy weight and give God the glory. Her struggle with her addiction to sugar is one shared by many. The newest dietary guidelines published by the Center for Nutrition Policy and Promotion state that less than 10 percent of our daily calories should come from added sugars. In the FP4H program, we don't like to refer to any particular food as "bad", since even sugar is fine in moderation; however, if sugar is a "trigger" food, then consider avoiding it. You'll learn in future chapters that my trigger foods are salty and savory: chips, crackers, and pizza, which I avoid. <u>Remember, food isn't sinful; people are.</u>

Apprentice with the Master Craftsman

The Lord restored me, stripped away the old me, sanded away the scars, and continues to add layers of protection. The result is an enduring finish reflecting the love and glow of Jesus. My first step was a willingness to act on what God wanted for me. I opened my eyes to my spiritual condition.

Take a few minutes to sit quietly in God's presence. Your invitation to wellness starts with seeing yourself as God sees you. Allow yourself to experience the hope that comes from knowing a loving God who wants freedom for you as you grasp His truth.

Admit your weakness. Pray for revelation about your reliance on food instead of God.

Claim God's truth. Ask God to strip away the sinful nature and release the fruit of His Spirit within you. Reflect on Philippians 4:13 and Ephesians 1:3-

14. Relinquish your willpower and request self-control through God.

Tell. Share your challenges with others. Find an accountability partner to share your journey.

Prayer:

Heavenly Father, I have denied, discounted, and dreaded bringing my weakness to you. You are faithful and true, waiting to hear from me. Lord, I cannot handle this on my own. I need you to come into my life and give me strength. Help me Lord to have confidence as you give me strength to receive the help I need to overcome this weakness in my life. Change me on the inside so restoration is evidenced on the outside. Thank you for your patience and love. Amen.

Devotions:

Acts 1 - Waiting for the Holy Spirit

Hebrews 4 - God's Promise and Your Faith

Acts 2:1-35 - Sensing God's plan

Hebrews 5 - Jesus' Obedience

Acts 2:36-47 - Change Your Life

3.
Fill in the Grooves

If nothing changes, nothing changes.
Meaning that unless I have thoughtfully and prayerfully considered how I
ought to live and act differently,
I'm likely to make the very same mistakes again next time.

–Clare De Graaf

When restoring an aged floor, deep scars require extra effort and expertise.
I learned to first touch a crumpled damp rag to the gouge while, at the same
time, applying the hot tip of an iron to the rag. The extra steam puffs the
wood back to the surface. In some cases, the deeply scarred grain requires a
second technique: Fill the groove with drops of rubbing alcohol then touch
the marred surface with the tip of a clean soldering iron. If all else fails, fill
the remaining dents with a slightly darker-colored wood filler.

*

At the inaugural meeting of leading my church's weight-loss ministry,
I found myself standing in front of the room, excited to be doing
something I knew God wanted yet scared to fail. I felt equal parts
vulnerable and empowered.

"I am starting this group because I need it," I shared. "I am learning right alongside of you."

That first meeting was eye opening for all of us, as we assessed our individual situations. We each took a "before" photo, weighed in, and recorded our chest, waist, hips, thighs and arm measurements. I faced the grim truth as the camera, scale and tape measure captured my current reality. For the first time in years, I really looked in the mirror and faced my condition. I knew I was in for a tough trip, a lifetime journey. I needed to learn an entirely new way to live.

So, how do any of us restore the beautiful body beneath the extra or excessive pounds of fat? Statistics show us that dieting is not the solution. One report from the National Institutes of Health indicates that one-third to two-thirds of us regain the weight within one year after weight loss, and almost all regain it after five years.[1] Studies also show that most dieters regain more weight than they've lost.[2] I fit that category; the more I dieted, the heavier I became. Those choosing surgical solutions report that after a year post-surgery, the weight lost gradually returns; 10 years out, the failure rate exceeds 20 percent for those who were originally morbidly obese and nearly 35 percent for those super obese.[3]

The thousands of dieting options overwhelmed me over the years, as I'm sure it has for many others. Nothing in my life had changed as I attempted one plan after another. My weight continued to be my biggest obstacle to wellness. Failing so many times, I'd eventually given up, refusing to fight the unbalanced scales—that is, until I found balance through First Place 4 Health.

---

[1] http://www.ncbi.nlm.nih.gov/pubmed/1580453
[2] http://www.ncbi.nlm.nih.gov/pubmed/17469900
[3] http://www.ncbi.nlm.nih.gov/pubmed/17060766

Finding My Balance With the Scale

First Place 4 Health challenged me to assess the balance I had in my life—not just physically but spiritually, mentally and emotionally. We need bravery when we assess ourselves to discover what is out of balance.

Balanced scales of any kind weigh equal on each side. Balanced audio, for example, requires a proper portion of bass and treble. When Vince installed surround sound in our home, he spent much time measuring the placement of speakers and wires, assuring that all were equal in distance and length. Also, thinking about the way our car tires need to be balanced, so do we need the balance of our loving God.

Do you sense the shimmy and vibrations from an improperly balanced life? Does the number on the scale determine your balance and worth? Even if this is so, there is hope. True success, a lifetime of rebalancing, occurs as we learn to live life and love God in the right proportions. Instead of yo-yoing up and down the scale, cycling on and off a diet plan, choose instead to find your courage and be brave.

When we choose not to address our wellness problems, we are, in a word, cowardly. How many of us long for the Lord to provide us with a new life, yet are unwilling to change old habits? Author Robert Mulholland writes in his book *Invitation to a Journey:* "The process of being conformed to the image of Christ takes place primarily at the point of our unlikeness to Christ's image. God is involved with us in the most imprisoning bondage of our brokenness. God meets us in those places of our lives most alienated from God."

When we realize that we are the least Christ-like, we are ready to allow Christ to provide balance in our lives. We are willing to change.

If You Want Something New, You Must Try Something New

If you want God to do something new in your life, you, too, must be willing to do something new. Jesus reminds us that God already has a plan for our lives. When asked, "What is the greatest command?" Jesus told us, "Love the Lord your God with all your heart and with all your soul and with all your mind and with all your strength." (Mark 12:30) Achieving full restoration requires all of our energy with all of our effort.

Loving God with all our hearts taps into our emotions. For those of us with food issues, we tend to cope with food instead of running to God. We eat when we are happy, sad, angry, tired, worried, bored or lonely. Our plan must focus on identifying emotional eating habits and triggers, then finding and developing new healthy emotional coping skills.

Loving the Lord with all our minds is what gives us mental health. How many thoughts run rampant in our heads, lies and untruths far from the thoughts of our Heavenly Father's? When crazy things pop into my mind, I rely on my memorized Scripture to ferret out the truth.

Possibly the hardest challenge of all is loving the Lord with all our souls. This requires us to embrace our bodies as a temple of the Holy Spirit. 1 Corinthians 6:19-20 challenges us with the question: "Do you not know that your bodies are temples of the Holy Spirit, who is in you, whom you have received from God? You are not your own; you were bought at a price. Therefore, honor God with your bodies." As we grow spiritually and surrender to His will for our lives, including the care of our temple, we love Him with all our soul.

Finally, loving Him with all our strength requires engaging our physical selves. We strengthen our muscles and bones with intentional acts of physical activity. We consume food to nourish each reproducing cell. We rest each night to refresh our bodies. Weekly we should Sabbath, stop and enjoy God's provision in our lives. Loving the Lord with all our strength requires diligent and deliberate physical effort.

As I mentioned, my sister introduced me to First Place 4 Health in 2005, and now I'd like to share with you a little background about it. Founded in 1981, this plan has a solid track record of success. While many other weight loss programs might say the same, I've tried many plans and FP4H is the one that has truly worked for me, as I will document on these pages. While I believe that each individual needs to find and feel good about whatever weight loss plan they choose, I can advocate for FP4H from my heart because it provides a Christ-centered plan, in community with others, that addresses the whole person, not just the physical body. It takes into consideration the following aspects:

- Emotional: It provides support and accountability with others and investigates the root of emotional eating.

- Spiritual: It recognizes that we need God's power to restore us. We turn our will and our lives over to the care of the Lord.

- Mental: We learn, practice and reinforce healthier eating and physical activity habits. All of this changes your mind about the concept of wellness.

- Physical: We strengthen our bodies with regular activity and exercise. We rest our bodies daily and weekly. The FP4H's Live IT© plan is based on the USDA's dietary guidelines and feeds the body with a balance of all food groups: fruits, vegetables, grains, lean protein, calcium-rich foods and healthy fats.

A Lifelong Plan, Rather Than a Quick Fix

He who has a why can deal with any what or how.
–Stephen Covey

Perhaps FP4H's plan is right for you. Alternatively, you will learn of other weight loss and wellness plans from the success stories in this book. (See the Appendix for a list of all plans mentioned throughout the book.) Whether you choose this or another plan, let's first review what types of plans to definitely avoid. Web MD suggests avoiding anything that:

- Promises quick weight loss

- Sounds too good to be true

- Gives simplistic conclusions drawn from a complex study

- Makes recommendations based on a single study or only testimonials

- Makes dramatic statements refuted by reputable scientific organizations

- Lists "good" and "bad" foods

- Makes recommendations based on selling a product

- Makes recommendations based on studies published without review by other researchers

- Gives recommendations from studies that ignore differences among individuals or groups

- Eliminates one or more of the five food groups

Now that we know what not to do, let's focus on choosing a proper plan. God's plan is best. In the book of Haggai, the Bible tells how the Babylonians decimated the city of Jerusalem when they raided, destroyed and carried the

Israelites off to Babylon the year prior. Now returned, the Israelites spent all of their time rebuilding the city, planting farms, fattening up the cattle, and ultimately focusing on themselves. The Lord's temple remained a pile of rubble. The Israelites had adopted a "me first" lifestyle instead of following God's plan.

God sent them a message through the prophet Haggai. God pointed out that they had spent all of their time on themselves and His house—the temple—was still in ruin. He told them to consider their ways and inspect their actions to honor His temple. How often do we work on everything and everybody else and neglect our own bodies, God's temple? God yearns for control of your personal temple restoration, too.

Remember that your weight loss, ironically, is not about food. Most of us know the proper quantity and quality of foods to choose. We also know physical activity strengthens our bodies. Yet we've repeated unhealthy behaviors for years, even decades. We need to learn, practice and ultimately change to new healthy behaviors for a lifetime. Surrender your lifetime plan to the one who loves you most: God.

True Measure of Success: Patrick Thayer

Before and after

I met Patrick Thayer at a FP4H event in Cincinnati, Ohio in 2012. I asked him to share in his own words the hard work of discovering a plan and staying on track.

My main stumbling block in life has always been my excess weight. I started a diet many times in the past and I did lose weight. Within a short time, I would gain all of it back, plus more. All of the yo-yo dieting took a toll on my health. I had high blood pressure, a hiatal hernia, sleep apnea and high cholesterol, and took five prescription medications a day.

In January 2006, at age 50, I joined First Place 4 Health through my church. I soon found that it was not a diet plan but a Live IT© plan. We put Christ first in our lives, including what we eat. We also trust in Him to help us with our physical activity. In the first year, with God's help, I lost more than 100 pounds.

When I began exercising, I had a hard time walking up the stairs without losing my breath. I started attending the YMCA to walk on a treadmill. My goal—one mile—turned into a 20-minute struggle. My knees hurt, mostly because of being overweight and having past knee surgeries that removed all the cartilage from my left knee and half from my right knee. Within the first year of beginning my exercise routine, I slowly increased to four miles in less than an hour on the treadmill. I worked out with various exercise machines four to five days a week. Losing weight and exercising changed my attitude. Getting up early to exercise was a struggle I battled with prayer. To this day, I pray each morning for Christ's strength as I rise from bed and drive to the YMCA at five o'clock.

I also pray every day that God will help me in my food choices. I am a foodaholic. I need God's help every day to choose the best food for meals and snacks. It's not possible to avoid food; we need it daily to survive. The temptation to overeat and choose the right foods is a constant battle.

In December 2006, about a year into my FP4H journey, a friend challenged me to complete a marathon. Impossible! I thought to myself. I bought and read the book *Marathoning for Mortals*. With God's help and the book's training plan, I began my plan to run in the Cincinnati Flying Pig Marathon in May 2007. It was amazing! With prayer and God's help in training, I completed my first marathon. In 2017, 10 years later, I completed my 22nd.

I thank God, my friends and family, the First Place 4 Health program and the YMCA for helping me change my life. Thank you Lord and Savior Jesus Christ. He continues helping me daily.

* * *

Since 2007, Patrick has maintained his healthy weight following God's plan. He made the first step in finding a plan. Next, he looked at his life and acknowledged what needed to change—and he did it! He tried something different and got different (positive) results.

Assessing the Condition

Let the morning bring me word of your unfailing love,
for I have put my trust in you.
Show me the way I should go, for to you I entrust my life. (Psalm 143:8)

Often we focus on the physical aspects of the self-assessment: weight, blood pressure, the ratio of our waist to our hips and chest. Yet the mental, emotional and spiritual aspects are every bit as important. I've compiled the following wellness assessment that asks questions about your lifestyle habits. Your answers will provide an overview of your wellness and help pinpoint steps that you can take to improve your overall balanced lifestyle.

Each of these areas is addressed in the upcoming chapters. Your responses will help you focus on the chapters that have the most importance in your wellness journey. The assessment takes approximately 15 minutes to complete. You will sub-total your scores in each section. Beware of comparing yourself to others. This is not a competition. There is no such thing as pass or fail. We are each on our own journey.

Balanced Lifestyle Wellness Assessment

Pray and ask the Lord where you are with each question. When you are honest, this tool will help you evaluate your balanced lifestyle, as well as your strengths and weaknesses. As you read each question, circle the number below the appropriate answer.

With all Your Heart = Emotional   **Score**

I control my emotions and express them appropriately.

Rarely	Seldom	Sometimes	Often	Very Often
0	1	2	③	4	_____

I protect myself from other people who dispose unhealthy emotions inappropriately.

Rarely	Seldom	Sometimes	Often	Very Often
0	1	②	3	4	_____

Weekly, I experience genuine community—fellowship with other believers through accountability, prayer and encouragement.

Rarely	Seldom	Sometimes	Often	Very Often
0	1	2	③	4	_____

I handle day-to-day stresses without feeling guilty about my food choices.

Rarely	Seldom	Sometimes	Often	Very Often
0	1	2	③	4	_____

Each day, I find time to relax and laugh.

Rarely	Seldom	Sometimes	Often	Very Often
0	1	②	3	4	_____

With all Your Mind = Mental   **Score**

I enjoy a healthy self-image, seeing myself uniquely designed to love and serve the Lord.

Rarely	Seldom	Sometimes	Often	Very Often	
0	1	(2)	3	4	_____

I set realistic goals, develop and follow a plan for success.

Rarely	Seldom	Sometimes	Often	Very Often	
0	(1)	2	3	4	_____

Daily, I account for my food intake and exercise using some type of tracking tool or daily log.

Rarely	Seldom	Sometimes	Often	Very Often	
(0)	1	2	3	4	_____

I recall memorized Scripture in difficult situations to overcome temptation, get guidance and transform my mind.

Rarely	Seldom	Sometimes	Often	Very Often	
(0)	1	2	3	4	_____

Daily, I consciously make an effort to thank the Lord and practice gratitude.

Rarely	Seldom	Sometimes	Often	Very Often	
0	1	2	3	(4)	_____

With all Your Soul = Spiritual   Score ₃

On a typical day, I spend the following number of minutes in devotional time with the Lord.

0-5	6-15	16-30	31-60	61+	
(0)	1	2	3	4	_____

I pray regularly (day/week) by name for the salvation of my unbelieving friends and family members.

Rarely	Seldom	Sometimes	Often	Very Often	
0	(1)	2	3	4	_____

I pray regularly (day/week) for the members in my accountability/small group of Christian believers.

Rarely	Seldom	Sometimes	Often	Very Often	
0	(1)	2	3	4	_____

Weekly, I intentionally spend time with unbelievers to build relationships and share Christ with them.

Rarely	Seldom	Sometimes	Often	Very Often	
0	(1)	2	3	4	_____

Before putting any food, drink and drugs in my body, I ask the Lord if it will honor my body.

Rarely	Seldom	Sometimes	Often	Very Often	
(0)	1	2	3	4	_____

With all Your Strength = Physical   Score

Daily, I eat nutritionally balanced meals, divided up by at least three meals, which includes one meal eaten up to two hours after waking.

Rarely	Seldom	Sometimes	Often	Very Often	
(0)	1	2	3	4	_____

In a typical week, I spend the following number of days doing 30 minutes or more cardiovascular exercises.

0 days	1 day	2-3 days	4-5 days	6-7 days	
(0)	1	2	3	4	_____

In a typical week, I spend two to three days doing 20 minutes or more of strength-training exercises.

Rarely	Seldom	Sometimes	Often	Very Often	
(0)	1	2	3	4	_____

Daily, I spend time gently stretching my body to improve flexibility and balance.

Rarely	Seldom	Sometimes	Often	Very Often	
(0)	1	2	3	4	_____

I get sufficient time to rest daily and a day of rest weekly.

Rarely	Seldom	Sometimes	Often	Very Often	
(0)	1	2	3	4	_____

Add up a score for each area and write them below.

Emotional Score

Mental Score

Spiritual Score

Physical Score

We experience smoother and less bumpy forward movement when we focus our efforts to balance out our scores. Briefly describe your condition for each of the four areas, identifying what issues are relevant to your strongest and weakest areas. If you are balanced, share what contributes to your balance.

Emotional:

Mental:

Spiritual:

Physical:

Apprentice with the Master Craftsman

Over time on your weight loss plan, you will strengthen in your weaker areas. Return to the assessment throughout your restoration journey, celebrating the transformation. (We will talk more in a later chapter about the importance of celebrating along the journey.) Consider recording your score on a sticky note with a date, or record it in a journal where you can keep track of changes over time. If you love data, start a spreadsheet!

Prayer:

Lord your Word directs us to repent, then, and turn to God, and you will wipe out our sins and you may provide times of refreshing (Acts 3: 19). We are undoubtedly miserable over our condition. We are ready Lord, for restoration. Renew a right spirit in us, as we prepare to undertake changes to glorify you. In Jesus name, we pray. Amen.

Devotions:

1 Corinthians 1 - God's Wisdom

Luke 9:1-36 - Stop Running Away

1 Corinthians 2 - God's Spirit and God's Power

Luke 9:37-62 - The Healing Power of Jesus

1 Corinthians 3 - You Are God's Temple

De-Junk Your Pantry and Track Your Progress

Have I not commanded you? Be strong and courageous. Do not be afraid;
do not be discouraged, for the Lord your God will be with you wherever you go.
(Joshua 1:9)

Rolls of musty carpet and broken furniture stand curbside, at attention, waiting for trash collection. We are now in the phase of our full body re-do where we need to clear the way and prepare for the next phase in restoration. When working on a flooring project, I've noticed how refinishers remove the quarter-round moldings from the edges of the room and apply painter's tape to the baseboards. This protects them from being accidently scratched by the floor sander. We will do a similar version of this prep work in the next phase of our weight loss journey.

*

During each FP4H meeting, we spend time learning a new habit or skill. One of the most important ones that I learned was tracking my food intake. My obvious girth was proof that I did not have a healthy perspective on when to stop eating, and I've found that tracking my intake helps my mind to understand when enough is enough. As I'm sure you can relate, tempting foods surrounded us at every angle. When I opened my kitchen pantry early in my FP4H journey, glistening bags of chips begged to be open. Boxes of savory crackers promised crisp and salty flavor. Chocolate bars stood at attention next to marshmallows and graham crackers, ready for a microwave s'more. My desk drawer at the office used to include my favorite treats, stashed away for my eyes only. When I first approached my family about removing all offending foods from our household, I was met with resistance.

"What do you mean we can't have chips in the house?" my husband and then teenage sons complained. We were all obese and needed to lose weight. I'd started this journey many times before, and I knew they thought if they resisted or waited long enough, I'd give up. I'd given up every other time.

For me, it is nearly impossible to eat one serving of chips. Most labels suggest 12 to 15 chips. Stop at 15? Not! Chips seemingly call my name from the pantry. After multiple failed attempts during the first two weeks after starting FP4H, I realized that remaining in control (not eating chips) required stopping them from entering the house. Try this: Consider the items in your grocery cart as the future contents of your stomach (which is exactly what they are). Before you enter the checkout line, scan your cart and ask the Lord if the food you've chosen brings honor and glory to your body.

For each of us, different things trip us up. For you, it might be chocolate, ice cream, candy or cheese. For me, along with chips, I struggle with crackers and cookies, as well as ice cream, so these are the items that I've designated as not having entrance into my fridge, freezer and pantry.

The change in my grocery buying habits seemed sudden to my family, even though they were well aware that I had begun (yet) another weight loss program. In the past I'd given up early on in the process. Since I persisted with my healthy habits, they took notice. While preparing dinners, I choose smaller portions on my plate, cooked extra vegetables for myself, and avoided the foods that my family continued to eat such as pizza, bread that was not whole grain, and fruit juices. The good news is that everyone agreed that for a short time, our home would be free of the foods that I struggled with the most. Yes, I stopped purchasing chips and crackers altogether and replaced ice cream with frozen yogurt or ice milk.

My family had watched me start and stop a diet for decades. At first, they hoped that if they waited long enough, I would, like many times before, give in and restock the pantry with the unhealthy snacks they loved. My being "forever changed" was not something that they had ever experienced (nor had I at that point). Yes, all of us were overweight, but it was not my place to suggest that they needed to lose weight. Likewise, I'm thankful that my husband never suggested that I lose weight or complained about my appearance.

One time, after I'd lost all the weight, he found an old picture of me lying on my desk and asked, "Honey, who is this in the picture?"

"That's me," I replied.

"No, it's not!" He snapped back at me, looking as if I had insulted myself.

I smiled. "Yes honey, you used to kiss that person. It's me at grandpa's house in his dining room."

He shook his head in disbelief. I loved him more than usual that day. I'm blessed and I know it.

Eventually, chips began to reappear in our pantry, as my husband no longer wished to abstain from his favorite snack just because I was "dieting." This was actually a good thing. I found that as time passed, my self-control strengthened and those forbidden foods no longer lured me from the other room. When I did indulge, I read the labels and measured my portions out in a bowl. Honestly, I still struggle with my beloved chips at times, some days adding two or three servings onto my food tracker. The good news is that I no longer sit with the bag and eat with abandon.

Tracking Your Food Intake

As you begin your weight loss plan, you will for sure need a means to track your food intake. For the first four years while I was losing weight on the FP4H plan, I used their paper Live IT© Tracker. (This can be found in the back of their Bible studies or printable from their website, www.firstplace4health.com/resources/tracker.html.) As I closed in on my last 10 pounds, I benefited from several online apps that helped me to zero in on "calories in" and "calories out." I started out paying for Calorie King then moved to MyFitnessPal since it is free.

Once I lost the weight and began a maintenance plan, I realized that I had lost sight of the balanced food groups I had embraced with the Live IT© Tracker. The tracker apps had me focused on total calories and not the quantity I ate from each group: fruit, vegetables, grains, proteins, dairy and healthy oils. I returned to tracking my food groups and still kept my eye on overall calories.

Research bears out the importance of food tracking. Studies show that people who keep a food diary six days a week lose almost two times as much weight as those who keep food journals one day a week or less.[4] How often people tracked their food was the best predictor of weight loss, with added success when those individuals attended a support group. In another study, those who kept daily food records lost twice as much weight as those who kept no records.[5] The options available to track our food are endless:

---

[4] http://www.webmd.com/diet/news/20080708/keeping-food-diary-helps-lose-weight
[5] http://www.sciencedaily.com/releases/2008/07/080708080738.htm

- The FP4H Live IT© Tracker tool keeps a record of your nutrition and physical activities. It also provides a section to measure your emotional state for the day (Happy, Sad, Angry, Tired), a space to record your memory verse for the week, and a section to record your spiritual disciplines: Bible reading, Bible study and prayer.

- The USDA SuperTracker records personalized nutrition and physical activity. This online tool available from the USDA website, www.supertracker. usda.gov, offers a database, called Food-A-Pedia, of nutrition information for a multitude of foods.

- IT developers release new calorie counters all the time. At this writing, my Android Play Store lists more than 100 food tracker apps. Find one that works best for you.

- A small notebook or journal works, too.

Once you find the tracker that works for you, use it. In the groups I lead, those who turn in a tracker to me each week are the ones who lose or maintain weight. Most of the time, if I'm not tracking, I'm gaining weight.

Overcoming Resistance to Tracking

Self-respect is the root of discipline: The sense of dignity grows with the
ability to say no to oneself.
—Abraham Joshua Heschel

Even though tracking is an important key for success, I struggled and still struggle today with doing it consistently. We need to strengthen our resolve when challenging situations threaten it. A wood floor is abrasion-resistant when it stands up to daily wear and tear. Consider the following solutions to your tracking challenges so that your tracking is abrasion-resistant and stands up to the daily wear and tear of life's circumstances.

Eating Out: During my childhood and teen years, eating at a restaurant, even fast food, was a treat or special occasion. Today, eight out of 10 Americans report eating out at fast food establishments at least monthly, with half stating that they eat fast food at least weekly.[6] Now an adult, I convinced myself that I was entitled to choose any food when eating out. I reasoned, "It's a special occasion and I should be able to eat whatever I want, right?" No, eating out should look as healthy as eating at home.

> **Solution:** Tracking food became my safety net when eating out. I make wiser choices when I compare the restaurant's menu with my food tracking app.

I'm Stressed: I've never heard anyone say, "I'm so stressed. I think I'll eat a salad." No, we want salty, crunchy or sweet snacks, and possibly all three. When my mind is not focused on my habits due to stress, I eat without consideration of the consequences. This, in turn, makes me more stressed!

> **Solution:** Tracking food helps me choose food within my healthy limit no matter my mood or stress level.

I Don't Have Time: When we dismiss tracking because of hectic schedules, we allow outside forces to control our situation. When I neglect my food diary, amnesia sets in and I forget, thereby blowing through my healthy limit.

> **Solution:** Commit to write it if you bite it.

I Don't Want To: We would rather remain in the dark than face the

---

[6] http://www.gallup.com/poll/163868/fast-food-major-part-diet.aspx

truth about what we are eating. We give up what we want most for what we want right now.

> **Solution:** Pray and ask the Lord to change your "I don't want to" into "Lord, I want to for You." Each prayer invites the Holy Spirit to govern your mind and strengthen you spiritually.

Anytime that I take a break from tracking, thinking that I must know my limits by now, I gain weight. When I record my dietary intake, I have greater success with my food choices. It's that simple, really. I find peace when I've documented my food choices at the time of my meal and ultimately honor God with my body. (1 Corinthians 6:19)

The bottom line is that we must know what we eat if we want to learn how to change. Tracking food works, so I recommend it as tool in your weight restoration toolbox.

True Measure of Success: Lisa

Before and after

Since my friend Lisa surrendered to God's desire for a healthier life, she's lost 160 pounds and has maintained a healthy weight since then.

I was always a good eater. I enjoyed good food and in the beginning, gained and lost weight, remaining at a healthy weight. Without a doubt, I was an official yo-yo dieter. When I got married, had children and advanced in age, the weight was harder to take off. How I looked wasn't as much of a priority as when I was younger. I tried several diets, all ending the same way: regaining the weight. I lost large amounts of weight but never kept it off. Now severely overweight, I knew I needed help.

Even though I had rededicated my life to the Lord, I was unsuccessful at keeping my weight off. Looking back, I see that the Lord helped me identify the root of my obesity. I was an emotional eater. When I sensed that the Lord wanted me to join a FP4H group in my church, I didn't want to do another diet, get on the scale, or follow a restricted food plan. At first, I only attended the meetings and completed the Bible study. Eventually, I modified the food plan, as the FP4H food plan seemed too strict for me.

As I worked through the studies, the Lord helped me embrace the food groups and make better choices, eating healthy and enjoying food without feeling deprived. Moderation was the key. I learned to trust God with my hunger.

After I lost a large portion of weight, my life spun out of control. I was losing my grip. The challenges of everyday life overwhelmed me. As I struggled, my thoughts turned to food. My weight began the upward climb. One day, while waiting at a stoplight, I knew in my spirit that God was calling me to a deeper walk. God revealed that He desired a healthy weight for me, more than I knew. I realized that only through Jesus would I succeed. The Lord was helping me again. I did this for His glory; apart from God, I could do nothing. Philippians 4:13 tells us, "I can do all things through Christ who strengthens me."

Jesus meets us at our level. Every day God finds me and puts me on the path of righteousness for his namesake (Psalm 23:3). When spending time with God in prayer and Scripture, I understand more of His character. The Lord gives wisdom liberally without finding fault (James 1:5). Every time a few pounds creep on, I increase my walking and I more intently watch my food intake. More importantly, I stay connected with the Lord in prayer and added accountability partners to my life. We help and pray for each other.

God has given me the benefit of health and weight loss. It is nice fitting into a size ten instead of a size 26. It is even nicer that I fit into normal seats again. Jesus came that we can have life and have it more abundantly (John 10:10).

* * *

Each time I talk with Lisa, we share our battles with staying on track with our maintenance. A powerful prayer warrior, she prays for us with this prayer: "Seek God, embrace His grace and accept His mercies."

Learning to Love Limits

Several years ago while attending a conference, the speaker asked, "Who has the most speeding tickets?"

I raised my hand to ask for clarification. "Over what period of time?"

The room erupted with laughter. There seemed to be no doubt; I was the winner of the most speeding tickets. As we know, police officers issue speeding tickets when we exceed the posted limit. Living life at full throttle, I struggle with limits—both in my car and in my food intake.

The problem is that obstacles bring us to a halt when we exceed our limits and, in my case, they resulted in injury and residual scars. At five years old, I was joyfully running full speed down a boat pier when I tripped on a board and ripped open my left knee. The scar was so big that I can still see the 10 stich marks decades later. At 13, my sister and a friend decided that all three of us should swing across a ravine together on the heavy knotted rope hanging from the trees. We were thankful that the rope held all of our weight as we swung from one side to the other. We made it across safely until a jagged tree root protruding from the ground, badly gashed my thigh. While in the emergency room, I had a sense that my future held more pain, more stitches and as of that day, another reminding scar. At 16 as a new driver, I plowed into a parked car. I was physically okay. My insurance policy had a high deductible, which left a huge scar on my wallet.

My full throttle experiences continued. At 18, a car cut me off as I exited the expressway. I slammed on the brakes and my car spun out of control. The momentum threw me across the bench seat (this was before the days of seatbelt laws) and I slammed against my friend in the passenger seat. The next few moments flowed in an eerie slow motion. The car, now sideways on the expressway, rocketed across six lanes of traffic without a driver. Through the grace of God, I caught sight of an 18-wheeler coming at us head on, so I forcibly lunged myself back into the driver's seat, gripped the wheel and veered the car away from imminent destruction. Only God knows why we survived. Lesson learned. I always wear my seatbelt and obey reduced speed limits on exit ramps. I am thankful for the later invention of anti-lock brakes.

Many of us have emotional and physical scars resulting from years of living outside of our healthy limits. We place ourselves in harm's way by going too far afield. My battle with maintaining my weight comes with a daily review of "calories in" versus "calories out." I know my limits and when I've gone beyond them. My tracker is the speedometer for my food choices. It tells me when I've gone too fast with my food intake. Yet, I am in a constant love-hate relationship with my tracker.

Other limits in life may be easier to maintain: faithfulness in your marriage, refraining from murder when we are angry, and living within our means. Yet as "dieters", we rail against food limits, struggling with and even refusing acknowledgement of them. Author Barb Raveling in her book, I Deserve a Donut, calls these limits "lifelong boundaries": "Lifelong boundaries in the area of food make our lives better because they keep us safe," she writes. "Yes, they cramp our style, but you know what? Our style needs to be cramped. Because there are consequences to eating 'what we want when we want.' Here are a few of them: Clothes that don't fit. Discomfort. Diabetes. Sore joints. Weight gain. Depression. Heart disease. Hopelessness. An early death. These are just a few of the enemies that lurk outside the 'fence' of our boundaries waiting to destroy us."

Paul writes in Ephesians 2:4-5: "But because of his great love for us, God, who is rich in mercy, made us alive with Christ even when we were dead in transgressions—it is by grace you have been saved." A transgression is violating a law, command or moral code, to offend, sin and go beyond the limits. Transgressions remind me that I am not the rule follower that I claim to be. Each time we exceed the limit, we are offending and sinning. Loving limits changes our perspective.

How ready are you to love the healthy limits in life? We must seek better options in our society of oversized convenience. Healthy options are available. Most restaurants will hold the butter, put salad dressing on the side, offer grilled food instead of fried, and substitute a vegetable instead of a high starch potato or rice. When ordering at my favorite Thai restaurant, I request the sauce on the side and swap zucchini or green beans for the side of rice. Most of the time, by dinner, I've already exceeded my daily grains limit, so I must say "no" to the rice. Be willing to pay extra for the changes and thankful when the swap is no charge. My "healthy lady" status can be testified wherever I eat by the wait staff and restaurant owners in my community. Who says eating out can't be healthy? It's a choice to remain within your limit.

To continue our floor restoration analogy, these changes that we make in our food and beverage choices are similar to the major overhaul that happens when we refinish wood. The sand paper grit is tough (tough love, perhaps?), with lots of big particles coming off the wood as the finish is sanded. Honestly, these are big changes and not ones that I lovingly embrace all the time. Yet, the adopted changes provided steady results for me, as I know they can for anyone who commits to them.

In my first 12-week session on the FP4H plan, I lost 17 pounds. The next session, I lost another nine, hitting my first milestone at 25 pounds. I did not lose weight each week. Some weeks I lost one or two pounds. Other weeks, the scale remained the same or displayed a small gain. In the past, I lost weight fast, 10 to 20 pounds in a month. When the weight loss slowed and my disappointment on the scale left me frustrated, I stopped my healthy habits and gained the weight back plus additional pounds. For the first time in my life, I was making "forever changes" with the FP4H approach and I was determined to keep the weight off. Even when weeks passed by and I didn't lose a pound, I didn't give up. Instead of frustration, I praised the weight that I was maintaining.

Removing that first large layer of fat, we steadily progress to the bare surface of our temple. When we refinish a floor, we stop and sweep up all the excess debris cluttering the workspace. There are many layers to clear out before moving onto a higher grit sand paper. This higher grit results in more subtle changes with a little less cleanup, which equates to a little less pain on our wellness journey.

Apprentice with the Master Craftsman

When we surrender and trust in God, we change. The spirit of God transforms us, and we are no longer motivated by fear and self-protection. We confidently approach God. Our heart finally embraces the truth our brain knows.

Are you ready for change? Lord we ask for your prompting, show us the change you want in my life at this time?

Do you need help tracking? Ask God to bless your food and your tracker. Ask Him to help you choose healthy foods.

When we allow the Lord to take control, we are more willing and able to change. When we do it out of love for our Father, we turn the world upside down. As we transform, others stand and wonder if they can have it, too. Absolutely, the first step is being willing.

Where are you struggling with limits in your life?

What accountability can you put in place to help you live within the limits?

Prayer:

But I have prayed for you, Simon, that your faith may not fail. And when you have turned back, strengthen your brothers. (Luke 22:32)

Heavenly Father, forgive us for the times we have resisted tracking and allowed our flesh to govern our mind. Lord, you are our strength; your Spirit gives life because of your righteousness. Help us to allow Your Holy Spirit to govern our mind. Thank you for the resulting peace and healthy life. Amen

Devotions:

1 Corinthians 4 – Everything You Need

1 Peter 1:1-13 – The Power of the Holy Spirit

1 Corinthians 5 – Spiritual Pride

1 Peter 1:14-25 – Exercise Self-control

1 Corinthians 6 – The Temple of the Holy Spirit

Part Two

Rough Sand, Strip And Reveal the Sub-Layers

De-Stressing

Be diligent in these matters; give yourself wholly to them,
so that everyone may see your progress.
(1 Timothy 4:15)

The buzz of the electric sander notifies the neighborhood that our restoration project is under way. The coarsest sandpaper levels the floor and tackles the gouges. The tedious work requires extreme caution. White knuckles grip the powerful sander as it grumbles with each pass back and forth across the floor. How long before the beautiful grain emerges?

*

Hitting my first weight-loss milestone underwhelmed me. I lost 25 pounds and the program suggested that I should celebrate the 10-percent body weight reduction. Who cares? I still had 91 pounds to go. I'd been there before. Big deal.

This time was different, though. My program challenged me to identify a non-food related reward that I could gift to myself. Because I was the leader of my weight-loss group, I led by example. I settled on treating myself to a luxurious full body massage. During this massage, I relaxed fully and thanked God for the weight loss. I enjoyed this indulgence so much that I decided I would get a massage each time I hit a 10-pounder goal—one at 228, 218,

208, 198 and so on, all the way to 158. As the masseuse kneaded my body, I begged the Lord to continue my physical restoration. I learned to praise my progress with each passing pound. Over the long journey, each massage came to symbolize a glorious reward for keeping to my limits and having "this time" be different.

I met Rich Kay when I visited and spoke at Pastor Steve Reynolds' church, Capital Baptist, in Annandale, Virginia. This church hosts "Losing to Live" wellness competitions, as outlined in Pastor Steve's book, *Bod 4 God*. I love how Rich practices praise.

True Measure of Success: Rich Kay

Before and after

It's been over 10 years since I lost 100-plus pounds, never to find them again. I no longer take a rainbow of prescribed drugs. No more sleep apnea. No more high cholesterol. No more borderline diabetic. No more fatty liver. I thank God often for the strength, wisdom and motivation to maintain this loss and improvement in my health.

So how did I go from years of yo-yo dieting and trying the latest pill, potion or piece of plastic exercise equipment with promises of overnight weight loss success to maintaining this loss of 100-plus pounds for more than seven years? Three words: small, simple changes.

My first one was getting on my knees and asking God for help. I was simply sick and tired of being sick and tired. I wanted to live, not exist. Losing 100 pounds seemed so overwhelming at first. It was the weight of two of my grandkids combined. I took refuge in and claimed Philippians 4:13 as my life verse: "I can do ALL things through Christ who strengthens me." I took it one day and one small, simple change at a time.

To stay motivated and keep the momentum of my weight loss journey, I needed positive feedback. Like Helen, I celebrated progress incrementally. I praised God for my progress. I learned that weekly goals worked for a while. I also realized that the body adjusts and sometimes I would not lose any fat that week. That was frustrating at first. I began to celebrate progress of other measures of fat loss, such as my clothes getting looser, gaining more energy and feeling stronger and less flabby. I shifted my focus to celebrating 10-pound incremental losses in addition to weekly losses instead of the overwhelming100-plus pounds. Looking back, it was very motivating to go from 270 pounds to 260, 250 and so on.

Celebrating progress was important. I had my share of

setbacks, too. We all do. When we get a flat tire, we don't slash the other three tires and end our journey. We fix it and move on. Tomorrow is another day. Setbacks or thoughts of failure are never final. It is simply feedback. Feedback is your friend and the breakfast of champions. Celebrate your previous progress when you have a setback and move on.

One particular verse from the Book of Proverbs (Proverbs 27:17) sunk in during my journey: "As iron sharpens iron, so one person sharpens another." You need people around you for resolve and encouragement. You get sharper in your resolve by someone sharper than you in areas where you may be a bit dull or lack knowledge or expertise. You cannot sharpen a knife on a pillow. You need a special stone. Building resolve starts with your relationship with Jesus. Then your circle expands from there with encouragement from church, family, friends, co-workers, doctors, nurses, personal trainers, health coaches, magazines, books, audio programs and more.

You will experience discouragement. This is Satan at work. Remember that you can do ALL things through Christ who strengthens you (Philippians 4:13). Surround yourself with positive people and sources of inspiration. Praise your progress and celebrate small successes on your journey to a fit and healthy lifestyle. Start with a prayer then keep smiling and keep charging.

* * *

Rich chronicled his weight loss by writing in journals, where he documented and celebrated the changes he made every week, and adding one new change a week. As I read his journal entries, which he made into a book titled, *Small Simple Changes,* I joined in praising his progress. During week one, Rich decided to park his car farther away from his office door. The second week, he chose to eat slower and drink water before and after each meal. In week five, he added walking to the second floor at work. By week 25, he had continued to practice all 25 new changes and eventually reached his goal.

We can all take a cue from Rich's approach. Each week in our weight loss support groups, we need to set aside time to celebrate the positive changes. I caution leaders from focusing too much on just the weight loss. It is critical to celebrate other healthy outcomes. After all, we won't maintain the weight lost unless we've cemented the necessary lifestyle changes.

In my weekly FP4H group meetings, I ask people to acknowledge and praise the challenges and changes they made the prior week, no matter how unique. For instance:

- I tried broccoli for the first time, and I didn't puke or die… Yay!

- I walked for five minutes each day instead of zero minutes.

- I tracked my food for five days this week. Hooray! When it comes to tracking, it's important to praise, praise, praise.

Ask yourself, "What change happened this week?" Experience God's blessings as you praise Him for the changes you've made in your life. Your changes honor Him. Our Heavenly Father cheers from the sidelines, similar to the proud parent or grandparent when we hit the ball off the T-ball stand for the first time, then continuing to cheer when we make it to first base for the first time, second time and third time. Embrace the change and enjoy His praise from heaven.

When I look back at my weight loss, I averaged 25 pounds a year. If you told me at the beginning that it would take me four years to lose the weight, I'm not sure I would have started. When we are praising God and thanking him for what he is doing in our life, we are sticking to our guns and battling as we keep going. When we stop celebrating, we begin listening to the negative voices in our head and risk becoming sidetracked. We miss the blessing. To be honest, the journey is full of blessing after blessing. The journey itself is a blessing. Once you've mastered that fact, you are not just a weight loser but also a true winner.

Choosing to take care of your health and physical condition is a spiritual discipline. In the same fashion that we pray, read our Scripture, fast and observe silence, so is maintaining physical health. We are learning a new way to praise the Lord with the discipline of healthy choices for ourselves, the temple of the Holy Spirit.

Five Stages Towards Total Wellness

But I will sing of your strength, in the morning I will sing of your love; for you are my fortress, my refuge in times of trouble. You are my strength, I sing praise to you; you, God, are my fortress, my God on whom I can rely.
(Psalm 59:16-17)

Your path to wellness can essentially be divided up into five stages that are common for almost everyone: At the Beginning, On My Way, Halfway There, Almost to Goal and At My Goal.

At the Beginning

Every sojourner must start at the beginning. I fought the idea of starting on my weight loss journey for a full year before I finally surrendered to it. When you step up and say, "Yes, I will begin," you are taking one of the hardest steps in your life. It means that you have finally stopped listening to the negative voices telling you that it is impossible, and have looked to the

Lord, who tells us all things are possible through Him (Matthew 19:26). You are agreeing to change. God wants to change us, but we are the ones who must willingly change. Filled with excitement and a healthy dose of humility, celebrate your willingness to say "yes."

On the Way

At this stage, you are learning new things and trying out the changes. You long for the end and realize that you still need to reach the halfway marker. I can almost hear your negative self-talk at this point: "How can I celebrate when I've only traveled part way? I must wait until I've lost more, all, and more than all. I never made it before. Why celebrate now? I must wait to celebrate when I've lost a minimum of 50, 75, 100, or all of it."

That's like saying, "Maybe we should wait until Jesus comes back to celebrate." That's kind of crazy, right? If we could see, even for one second, where this negativity is leading us, would we follow? Not usually. Yet oftentimes we turn our backs on the truth and instead believe the lies we hear. When we are "On the Way", part of this leg of the journey is finding things to celebrate. Look at your journal and thank God for the changes He is making in your life right now, today. Hallelujah!

One of my friends started her journey at 337 pounds. When she lost 38 pounds and broke the 300-pound barrier, she celebrated, praised the Lord, and fought to stay in the 200s. Once or twice, she took the scale in the bathroom so that she could weigh in with her birthday suit. It was important for her never to see 300 on the scale again. Months later, I asked my friend to share her success story at an event. By then she was down in the 270s, having lost more than 60 pounds. She told me, "No, I don't feel like a success story." My shrieks of disbelief were the first signs of having a hissy fit. I thought, *What is up with people not able to see success in losing 60 pounds?* Yes, she still had another 100 to go. It is absurd to think that we must wait until we've lost 170 pounds to celebrate.

Halfway There

So, you've made more changes that you ever thought you could. Still, you need to make more. Yet, you can look back and see how different you are from when you were at the beginning. Another friend who was getting close to breaking the 199 barrier told everyone in our group that she was approaching One Hundred Land, her new wonderland. Imagine the hooting and hollering when she stepped on the scale that day and it read 199! We need to look forward to these milestones and rejoice. Figure out your halfway mark and make your party plans. Focus, press on and keep your eyes open to additional changes you will need to embrace and, yes, celebrate.

Almost to Goal

Okay, you've stuck with the weight loss plan. Perseverance was the key. As you close in on the goal, it appears harder to reach. Weariness sets in and we question if it's worth going the final stretch. When I had only 20 pounds left, people shared how great I looked. Some people expressed concern that I had lost too much weight even though my weight still ranked in the overweight category according to the Body Mass Index Table.

Our culture has grown accustomed to looking at overweight and obese people. When we approach our normal healthy weight, we become a reminder to others of their own health and wellness challenges. Their discontent translates to pressure on us to accept our current status. Celebration is important now, more than ever. You must deny the discouragement you might sense. I promise that when you reach out and call on the Lord, He knows exactly your location and your thoughts. Beware of backwards motion. We tend to criticize ourselves when we begin to regain weight that we fought so hard to lose. The mind games begin. The negative voices persuade us into thinking that the goal is impossible. At this point, we could cave in and accept defeat, giving up when we are ever so close.

At one point after reaching my goal, I found myself 15 pounds above it. In a dangerous place, I struggled to find something to praise. I went into battle mode devising a plan. I signed up for a triathlon sprint. I was thankful for the opportunity to compete, swimming a quarter mile, bicycling seven miles and running a 5K. This was my second year competing. The best part of it is the desire to train. For three months, I ran, biked or swam six days a week. My goal was to beat my time from the previous year. During the swimming portion of the race, as I was closing in on the shoreline, I realized that I was alone; no one was swimming around me. Mistakenly, since I focused on swimming fast, I had been swimming for at least two minutes towards shore on the wrong side of the final buoy. Risking disqualification, I turned around and retraced my swim to the correct side of the buoy. In the end, my swim clocked in at three minutes more than the prior year.

As I ran up the bank of the lake, I said to myself, "Thank goodness, that swim is over! Lesson learned: Keep my eye on the goal!" When we are almost at goal, we can risk losing track of why we started in the first place. In some cases, we move backwards before we can move forwards. As much as I dislike these life lessons, I choose to revel in what I've learned and move forward. Sometimes, the best path for us on the journey is the long way. Like Philippians 3:14 says, "Perseverance and finishing the race is what wins the prize."

At this stage, fear can threaten to paralyze us.

"What if I lose the weight and cannot remain at goal?"

"I am not sure about this new shape I see in the mirror."

"I might not ever make it. What kind of testimony is that?"

"I experienced a setback. Restarting is too hard. Everyone is watching."

Fear isolates us when we stop trusting the Lord. We dangerously set out on our own and our spiritual life dries up. We are thirsty for the truth yet we continue to wander as if in a desert. When you recognize a dry spell, reflect back on the progress you've made. Praise the Lord for the changes He has sprung up in your life. Jesus regularly referred to the everlasting water he provided. In John 4:13-14, He answered, "Everyone who drinks this water will be thirsty again, but whoever drinks the water I give them will never thirst. Indeed, the water I give them will become in them a spring of water welling up to eternal life." Celebrate what God is doing. Set your eyes on the goal and ask the Lord, "What's next? What new thing would you have me do?" Keep journaling and stay focused on your healthy goal.

At the Goal

You've finally made it! Yippee! You can now do the happy dance at the scale. Now what? When we turn around and look back, we realize that there is a new future, a new scary place. Reality sets in once more. We are in for another lifelong journey ahead, a battle maintaining the weight. Remember that this is not in our strength, but in His strength. Now is the time to continue to thank and praise God for the weight we've lost. We must stick to our battle plan and keep the thanksgiving posture we've been practicing; keep celebrating and reinforcing the positive.

Remember Shanda from an earlier chapter? She still rejoices in the change in her lifestyle. She loves the Lord by choosing healthy foods and spending time doing physical activity every day. She celebrates by implementing the next healthy change. I know that seems impossible to some of you. I promise, the more you praise your progress and thank God for the changes He does in your life, the easier it will be to repeat the healthy choices.

The Sons of Korah, musicians for the temple in Jerusalem, helped the Jewish people praise and worship God even when they were discouraged. Psalm 42:34 tells us, "My tears have been my food day and night, while people say to me all day long, 'Where is your God?' These things I remember as I pour out my soul: how I used to go to the house of God under the protection of the Mighty One with shouts of joy and praise among the festive throng."

When you are about to give up, when your lifelong journey from obesity to wellness seems too long, too hard and almost impossible, when you don't think you can lose one more pound, you must honestly pour out your thoughts to Daddy God. Remember what God has already done. I challenge you to praise the progress. Practice overflowing with God's blessings. Now, join me as we press onto the next stage in our restoration.

Apprentice with the Master Craftsman

Reflect on your own journey. What milestone should you celebrate? What challenges have you overcome? Who has helped and encouraged you? What stage has been the most difficult? Have you reached a stage that seems impossible or defies human ability? Is it possible that God is asking you to rely solely on Him? Allow God to fight for you.

Prayer:

Lord still my heart. You fight for me even when I struggle to praise the transformation in my life. Help me to remain focused, no matter what challenges come my way. Thank you for never giving up on me. Amen.

Devotions:

1 Timothy 4 – Our Hope is in the Living God

Psalm 139: 1-12 – God Sees Me and Knows Me

1 Timothy 5 – Don't Share in the Sins of Others

Psalm 139: 13-24 – I am Fearfully and Wonderfully Made

1 Timothy 6 – Pursue Righteousness and a Godly Life

6.
No Short Cuts

We remember our God and Father your work produced by faith, your labor prompted by love, and your endurance inspired by hope in our Lord Jesus Christ.
(1 Thessalonians 1:3)

Anyone who has refinished a wood floor knows that skipping any of the important refinishing steps will only lengthen the process. You've made it through what's called the "first cut", the initial sanding step with the coarsest grit sand paper. You've removed a layer of finish and it's left behind deep scratches. The next cut, with medium-grit paper, will even out the ridges. Subsequent sanding, with increasing finer abrasives, will smooth the wood. Eliminating any one of these sanding steps will result in a delay, since the finer sand paper will not remove the deep scratches from the prior step. It's an apt metaphor for our weight loss journey. When we follow each step in the proper order, our deliberate actions result in a successful restoration—of floor and "self."

*

This may come as a surprise to you (after having shared that I participate in triathlons) but I've never understood why or how people enjoyed exertion. For many years, the big "E" word hovered on the horizon of my lifestyle change-up. I wanted to skip this step entirely but information about how crucial it is abounded at every turn. Finally, I knew there was no getting around the fact that physical activity is an important contributor to maintaining a healthy weight. In my first year of weight loss, I shed 30 pounds and my knees no longer screamed in pain. My stamina and flexibility also improved. I no longer had an excuse; I needed exercise in my plan.

I'm obviously not the only person who ever felt this way about exercise. My friend Marian Swiss-Taylor shared in an email:

"I do not hate exercise. Wait . . . that is a lie straight from the pit of hell. I do hate it. I like the fact that exercise burns off calories. I like the cute exercise wear that is out now. I like the fancy gadgets that you can buy motivating you to exercise. Yet, I hate exercise. I hate the jumping up and down. I dislike the pounding of my feet on the street, or treadmill, or wherever I am. I rather detest sweating. The water dripping on my face and the sweat running down my back and chest freaks me out.

"Yesterday, I attended a water aerobics class after listening to my sister and a friend. 'Fun,' they said. They lied. You won't hurt when you join the class. They lied. You don't sweat when you do water aerobics, as the water keeps you cool. They lied. Toss on your suit and come. My older sister reports the women of different ages and sizes in attendance will allow me to fit in and not be self-conscious. She lied, lied, lied, LIED."

Needless to say, water aerobics didn't work for Marian. She doesn't like to swim and felt self-conscious. Marian also tried belly dancing, which she enjoyed. She also considered adult training wheels for the pretty blue bike that is now collecting dust in a corner of her garage. She did not give up. Instead, she confessed her frustrations to people who loved and encouraged her. We actually enjoyed her rants with each new physical activity she tried. Today, Marian still has not given up on exercise or on weight loss. She now leads the FP4H ministry at my beloved former church in Pittsburgh. I am thankful for her perseverance.

Ugh, exercise requires discipline. The Bible says, "No discipline seems pleasant at the time, but painful. Later on, however, it produces a harvest of righteousness and peace for those who have been trained by it" (Hebrews 12:11). Will exercise bring me righteousness and peace? Choosing discipline requires sacrifice. First, I needed to find the time. Second, I needed to stop whining. Third, I needed to stop avoiding and procrastinating. Like the Nike slogan says, I needed to "Just do it."

When we do something that God desires, we most often need to relinquish something that we desire. In order to fit exercise into my routine, I needed to wake up earlier. In 2008, 15 months after I started my weight loss journey, I stopped hitting my snooze alarm and began exercising early in the morning.

I wonder if strength is last on Jesus' list of how we love God with our hearts, minds, souls and strength (Mark 12:30) because it is the hardest discipline. Sharing my problem with God, I wrote in my weekly prayer partner request, "I want to want to exercise." I desired for my perspective to be changed. Why did I dread working my physical body?

Dance, Walk, "Wog", Run, Bike

Challenged to find something fun to do from my youth, I purchased a dance program for my sons' video consol.

"Please, Mom," their eyes rolled like typical teenagers, "never dance when our friends are around."

In spite of the continual dull pain in my knees, I danced. I softened the blows to my body with extra rugs under the dance mat. Each morning that I danced, my over-plumped body giggled. Too cheap to spend money on

XXL exercise clothes, sweat drenched my baggy pajamas. The weight slowly released from my body and my knees hurt less. I worked my way up from 10 minutes to 15 then 20 every day. Hooray for another answered prayer! By the fall of 2008, I'd lost 50 pounds and was dancing 20 minutes a day every Monday through Friday.

Until then I hid inside my home, away from the world, exercising where no one could see me. A day came when I wanted to walk outside. Starting the process again, I walked 15, 20 and 30 minutes each day. I bought a pedometer to measure my progress. Each weekday morning, my husband joined me in support. We walked two miles, the equivalent of 4,200 steps on my pedometer. I set my long-term goal—10,000 steps a day.

After two years of walking two miles a day, the walking seemed easy, almost boring. When I told my friend Joyce Ainsworth, she said in her sweet southern drawl, "Helen you should complete a 5K."

"Other people run those races, not me," I balked.

"Walk, run, jog . . . it doesn't matter," she encouraged. "Sign up for a race. You can do this."

I had bad memories of running from my childhood. I was always the slowest, at the back, the last one in. I'm still not a fast runner today. When I discovered that I burned more calories jogging than walking, the deal was sealed. I "wogged", which is what I call walking followed by jogging. At the time, I lived in Pittsburgh, Pennsylvania at the bottom of a hill. I started by walking uphill and jogging downhill. As my stamina increased, I wogged up the hill, jogged then walked. Eventually, I was able to jog up and down all the hills in the two-mile loop of my neighborhood. I was running!

Weather didn't stop me from sticking to my routine. The winters in western Pennsylvania require several layers of clothing with gloves, a scarf and a hat. I ran whenever the wind chill temperature was above 22 degrees and the roads were free from ice. If the sun had not yet risen, I wore a yellow neon vest and clipped a flashing light to my waist. I also ran against the traffic in the left lane. Who knew that a crisp morning run was a great way to start the day? Finally, I no longer loathed the "E" word.

My boredom with walking and running continued so Vince and I joined a bicycle group one April, three years into my weight loss journey. On our first Saturday, we rode 10 miles on a nearby trail. Each Saturday we added one or two to the previous week's total. In June, our group rode 30 miles. The ride took three hours and believe it or not, I had fun. Victory! Something had changed. I looked forward to each week's ride and dare I say: I actually wanted to do it.

The picture [left], taken in 2005, shows my XXL body riding a bike. I bought a sturdy bike with a big seat. It was fun and something I could handle. Today, I continue to ride. The photos on the right was taken six years later at the same spot on the Montour Trail in Pennsylvania. I loved riding bikes as a kid and still do as an adult.

Taking It to the Next Level With a Trainer

In 2010, after being on the FP4H plan for four years, I hired a personal trainer. Marianne specialized in helping inactive people become active. She worked one-on-one with me for over a year. She developed a specialized plan based on my weaknesses and needs. I met with her every two weeks and followed the strength and flexibility plan at home two times a week. It was money well spent. I am forever thankful for Marianne teaching me proper form, an important component of a balanced body. Instead of cardio every day, I changed my routine to three days of cardio and two days of strength training. She also suggested that I increase my cardio activity to 45 minutes per day to give my body an extra boost. *Oh boy,* I thought, *am I really paying for this torturous advice?*

In 2011, while attending a FP4H Wellness Week retreat, I discovered water aerobics. Unlike Marian, I took to it like . . . well, a duck to water. We laughed and enjoyed ourselves as we splashed our way through the cardio, strength and flexibility—all in one workout. Once home, I joined a gym and attended weekly water aerobics. Already wet, I added swimming for 15 minutes after my class. Afterwards, I rewarded myself with time in the sauna. As the water droplets disappeared from my body in the warm air, I'd reflect on my workout, the day, my family and thanked God for His abundant blessings. My friend Joyce continued her encouragement.

"Did you sign up for a race yet?"

"No, not yet." I responded each time she'd ask.

Then finally, inspired by her story, which she wrote about in *Food, Freedom and Finish Lines,* I signed up for the Turkey Trot a 5K race in my community on Thanksgiving 2012. In the gym, I trained with a new focus: I wanted to finish the race! Vince and I arrived early on race day to find a place to park, since more than 6,000 people were registered for the race. I missed the memo about wearing festive clothing. Turkey headbands and hats, pilgrim costumes, and even dogs were decorated.

When the starting gun fired, I had to wait my turn before running over the timing mat that measures each runner's start and stop time. I'd attached the timing chip to my waist, a rookie mistake. It's supposed to be worn on your shoe near the ground and the timing mat. Oops.

I'd read that the odds of running a good race are increased if you can see the finish line in your mind. I'd also learned to break the race into thirds; during the first third, your adrenalin is pumping and you must be careful not to run too hard. Check: My heart was definitely pumping hard. The race took us over the Roberto Clemente Bridge in downtown Pittsburgh, crossing the Allegheny River into the center of the city. When I looked back, I could see PNC Park perched on the shore where I had started and hoped to finish the race.

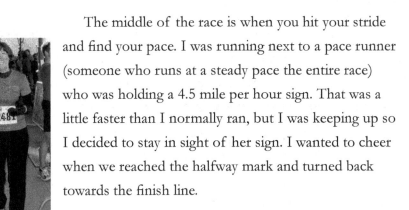

The middle of the race is when you hit your stride and find your pace. I was running next to a pace runner (someone who runs at a steady pace the entire race) who was holding a 4.5 mile per hour sign. That was a little faster than I normally ran, but I was keeping up so I decided to stay in sight of her sign. I wanted to cheer when we reached the halfway mark and turned back towards the finish line.

Many people were racing with others. I'm glad I was by myself. It gave me time to take it all in. If I'd been with another person, I'd be blabbing the entire time, and I knew that Vince was at the finish line waiting to cheer me on.

Most of the people were racing for fun, burning calories so they could eat a turkey feast later. Yet there were others who were serious about their race. At one point, a young runner in shorts sprinted past me. Brrr, it was 29 degrees outside. By contrast, I was bundled up with layers and mittens to keep my hands warm.

The last third of any race requires a steady pace to save your energy for a sprint to the end. Forget about sprinting; I only wanted to finish the race. It's a good thing that I'd practiced running on hills, as it was a steep climb to the top of the Roberto Clemente Bridge.

I never understood the phrase "It's all downhill from here" until I started running on hills. Yeah, it was all downhill to the finish line, which I joyfully passed with a big smile on my face. I was overwelmed with a sense of accomplishment. My training had paid off. It was official: I was a runner. Racing made sense now, as the competition gave me an incentive to train. Time to find another race!

Becoming a Triathlete

In March 2013, I met Sherry Leggett when I led a FP4H training seminar. She asked if she could arrive late because of a triathlon. After she arrived, Sherry beamed as she answered our inquiries about the race. We joined in celebrating her third place finish. Later, I took Sherry aside.

"Tell me more about competing in a triathlon. I'm interested. I swim. I bike. I run. Will you help me?"

That day, another encourager entered my life. Sherry shared all she knew. She sent me emails, Facebook private messages and texts with information to get me started. I stuck to an eight-week triathlon-training plan and worked out four to six hours a week. Now I understood why people sign up for races. I wanted to train so I could finish the race; however, once the race started, I realized that I didn't want to be last. I finished my first triathlon in 2013, seven years after I'd started my weight loss journey, and it was an incredible feeling. I placed 184th place out of 188 competitors. I beat a 23-year-old, 35-year-old and a 75-year-old, all women. Mission accomplished. I'd crossed over into the racing world. I was a true contender. Thank you, Sherry.

Since then, I've competed in 5Ks and triathlons each year. That first year after cheering for me on the sidelines, Vince decided to join me. That second year, we ran together while our son, Alex, cheered us on. The third year, Alex, 28 at the time, joined us in the race. In 2016, I trained hard and beat my best time in the July triathlon, my fourth year in a row, with my son, Davis, 26 years old, cheering me on.

The most glorious realization is that moving your body and feeling more fit is contagious and surprisingly empowering. The stronger I became, the more challenges I wanted to embrace. I am grateful that Vicki Heath, FP4H's national director and a long-time Body & Soul Fitness instructor, always included fun workouts at our events. (Body & Soul Fitness, established in 1981, offers exercise programs, choreographed to uplifting, upbeat contemporary Christian music; check out bodyandsoul.org.)

Subtly over the years, I sensed a prompting within me: *Become a Body & Soul Fitness Instructor.* Once again, my immediate disobedient and stubborn response was, "Lord, this is crazy. Someone else must be more qualified."

He was persistent. After all, He promises that all things are possible, right?

Body and Soul Obedience

In January 2014, while serving at Fun & Fitness 4 Life, a wellness weekend for women at Sandy Cove Ministries, a Christian retreat center in Northeast, Maryland, I sensed loud and clear that my next endeavor would include— you've guessed it— becoming a certified Body & Soul Fitness instructor. Divine power propelled me to do more than I could ever imagine. Yet, I hesitated, questioning how I would add this to my full plate. I wondered, *When will I learn to stop arguing with God?*

In obedience, I sent in my application to Body & Soul Fitness. They immediately provided me with video examples and instructions on how to submit videos of me leading four different workouts for my audition. In normal fashion, I stalled and dreaded the thought of videotaping myself. I procrastinated and waited until the last possible moment to complete my audition. In two weeks, I memorized four routines by practicing repeatedly for a few hours each day. I've never been a dancer or in the marching band, or done anything that prepared me for this new adventure. The choreography sheets seemed to be written in a foreign language. It took me several days to figure out that the boxes on the sheets corresponded to musical changes in the songs. (For example, Box B with squats always went with the chorus, and Box C with pliés went with the bridge.)

The video recordings were a great tool. I could see all the things I was doing wrong. After many deleted takes, even I could see my improvement. It wasn't perfect, but at least I looked like I knew what I was doing and I remembered to smile, too. In the end, Body & Soul Fitness approved me to teach their Strength and Flexibility program. That was only the beginning.

Now approved, I needed to get on the schedule at my church for a room for my class, advertise in the bulletin then learn 12 routines to teach. I am thankful for my church community, who welcomed me with open arms. People came to my class and, more importantly, they came back. The final step in the process was studying for my certification with the American Council of Exercise (ACE) as a Group Fitness Instructor.

The ACE certification exam required me to learn the essentials of exercise science and the human body. I purchased the ACE study materials, which included two textbooks, a DVD and practice exam. I studied for four months, four to five hours a week. I was so nervous the day of my exam that I asked Vince to pray for me before I got in the car to drive to the exam location. It took me two-and-a-half hours to take the test. I also said a prayer when I hit the submit button. Results are given immediately after completing the exam. With the energy searing through my body, I stood and held my breath as I waited for the screen to respond. When I saw the results, tears of joy streamed down my face. Hallelujah, I passed.

When it comes to obedience, I am a work in progress. Jimmy Seibert is a senior pastor and president of a ministry that starts churches all over the world. In his book, *The Church Can Change the World: Living From the Inside Out,* he says that a common question he and his wife would ask their children was, "How do we obey?" The couple taught their children to respond cheerfully, quickly and completely. I wasn't quick but I was cheerful and complete. I had no idea when I asked God to change my "want to exercise" that I'd end up being a certified fitness instructor. Many small steps led to a large leap into the fitness industry. God astounds me with His never-ending grace and patience with me!

At my first Body & Soul Fitness workshop in August 2014, in Laurel, Maryland, I roomed with an instructor who lived in London, England. Located all over the globe, I found our next success story on the African continent: Abagail from Zimbabwe. Her life changed when she started attending a Body & Soul Fitness class as a member. God is at work all over the world.

True Measure of Success: Abigail Zinyengere

Before and after

My journey began in April 2012 with a lot of crying, health issues and just being tired of life. I was depressed at how big I had become and, at the same time, the inability to change anything. I would tell myself, "I will lose weight soon." But, I kept gaining. The only thing I was losing was hope. People's comments didn't help, either. I often had someone asking, "When are you due?" Then one day out of desperation, tears running down my cheeks, I cried out to the Lord and prayed. I acknowledged that I was a failure on my own but with Him, I could do this. That prayer changed my life forever.

My God heard my cry. I was 105 kilograms [231 pounds]. Soon after my cry for help, someone suggested a detox for nine days to kick-start my weight loss. I told my husband about it and he joined me, also wanting to lose weight. I did the detox and I lost six kilograms [13 pounds]. The calorie-counting program required exercise and I increased my attendance at my Body & Soul Fitness class back home.

I had a number of diet options and I came up with a program that I felt was manageable and achievable. I eliminated bad carbohydrates and focused on healthy ones by introducing lots of vegetables and lean proteins into my meals. I followed my program and after one month, I was now at 90 kilograms [198 pounds] for a total weight loss of 15 kilograms [33 pounds]. Motivated, I kept asking for ideas from friends. The book Made to Crave by Lysa Terkeurst changed how I viewed food, as well as my relationship with God.

In six months, I weighed 80 kilograms [176 pounds], closing in on my goal of 78 kilograms [171 pounds], the ideal weight for my height of 1.78m [5'10"]. I worked hard but somehow the last two kilograms would not release. Someone suggested a slight change in my diet and physical activity. I continued with my Body & Soul Fitness classes and added jogging. That did the trick. I lost the four kilograms, thereby achieving my goal.

Knowing people lose weight and gain it back again, I had a quest to maintain my healthy weight. Body & Soul Fitness has been a pillar of strength. The instructors and class members encouraged me to keep at it. Body & Soul Fitness introduced a 12-week "Healthy and Whole" living program where the instructors, Kate and Leonie, took us through God's plan for health and food. The program helped me understand the difference between healthy and unhealthy foods. The information motivated me to choose God's way when I felt like overeating.

I have not mastered it all, but I am a much better person and my lifestyle is healthier than when I started. I strive for improvement in all aspects of my life and give glory to God for the journey. Today, I appreciate healthy living and am more energetic. Body & Soul Fitness has provided me with physical, emotional and spiritual fitness through workouts, devotions and fellowship with other ladies. I've made great friends who hold me accountable along my continuing journey of managing my weight.

* * *

Abigail said "yes" and asked the Lord for help on her journey. Any one of us can say "yes" to God and He will do amazing things. I'm proof of that, and so are the other success stories in this book. If God can change this stubborn, strong-willed, 274-pound woman with screaming knees into a triathlete and fitness instructor, He can change anyone. His power is not limited to a select few. Its transforming power is available to all. Just ask.

Getting Started with Your Exercise Plan

I started my exercise plan in the same way I learned to pray: timid and bashful at first. The more time I spent, the greater confidence I gained. Time spent exercising could be considered part of your prayer time if you are doing it to honor God. Start your physical disciplines in the same way with small steps:

1) Consult with your healthcare provider before starting a program. My

doctor was thankful that I wanted to increase my physical activity.

2) Discover something you enjoy. What did you enjoy as a child or your younger adult years? Was it riding your bike, swimming or dancing? Choosing different activities increases your probability of finding something you will keep doing.

3) Start low and go slow. My doctor, even now, cautions me. If we start out too high and fast, we risk injury and need to wait for our body to recover. I started with 10 minutes every day. Experts recommend three to five days a week. If I set a goal for three days a week, tomorrow was always the day I would start. I'd end up with one or two days of activity, rarely three. Do something every day.

4) Increase the intensity. When you complete an activity with ease, increase to the next level in difficulty. Consider increasing the length of time spent exercising, increasing your speed, or adding additional weights to your routine. Find a new challenge.

5) Strengthen your muscles, build sturdy bones and increase your metabolism. Different exercises use resistance to strengthen different muscle groups, such as upper body, core and lower body.

6) Develop your plan. The age-old saying, "If we fail to plan, we plan to fail" has some truth to it. When it is on your schedule, you will discover a way to check it off your list. A multitude of people and tasks compete for our time. Prioritize physical activity, adding it to your "to do" list of important items.

7) Track your progress. I'm more motivated when tracking my progress. Enlist a buddy and share your trackers. Accountability always helps.

8) Forgive yourself. God's mercies are new every morning (Lamentations 3:22-23 ESV). Restart when you have given up. Keep going.

So that is my story of conquering the "E" word. Now that I keep physical movement in my daily life, that letter stands for "energized." At the beginning, I would rather starve myself than exercise. My "2 x 4 moment" came when I realized that healthy people incorporate physical activity into every day. Since I didn't want to exercise, I asked the Lord to change my desires. In obedience, I tried new and different activities and my commitment grew. As my commitment grew, my discipline grew. As my discipline grew, my strength grew both physically and spiritually. It all made me curious: What else could God transform in my life if I were obedient?

Apprentice with the Master Craftsman

What barrier keeps you from strengthening your body? With our eyes focused on Jesus, nothing has the power to stop us from making God honoring changes in our life. What small action can you start today for moving your body?

Remember a time in your life when physical activity was fun. Remember where you were, how did it sound, and what were your feelings? What activity did you enjoy?

Who can encourage you with incorporating new physical activity in your daily plan? Recruit someone, sharing your goals, giving them permission to hold you accountable. Consider hiring a professional personal trainer.

Prayer:

Heavenly Father, your spirit made me. Your breath Almighty gives me life. You promise peace when I keep my eyes focused on you rather than the problems that keep me from moving forward in my wellness journey. Forgive me, Lord, for the times I resist the need to move my body for you. Help me identify your will in my life. Remove the distractions and barriers from my path. Thank you for giving me divine weapons with power, destroying all that opposes your word and nature. Lord, grant me peace, fill me with confidence, as I step towards wellness. Lord, I "want to want to" exercise. Amen.

Devotions:

Hebrews 11 – Faith in Action

Philippians 3 – Press on Toward the Goal

Hebrews 12 – No Discipline is Pleasant

Philippians 4 – All Things in God's Strength

Hebrews 13 – The Lord is My Helper

7.
Reclaimed Reality

Failures, repeated failures, are finger posts on the road to achievement.
One fails forward toward success.
—C.S. Lewis

Fine dust rises into the air as the wood's peaks and valleys disappear. The uneven and stressed wood, prone to tearing and gouging, requires patience. A thick buffer pad added between the sander and the medium grit sandpaper serves as a shock absorber. It flattens any remaining high and low points left behind from the previous step, doing so with a coarser grit.

*

Have you ever done something that you regret? Of course, you have. We all have.

Growing up, it was rare to see Mom and Dad without a cigarette in their mouths. My sisters' and my daily chores included emptying ashtrays. In 1968, my younger sister, Kathy, came home from second grade and pleaded with our parents, "Please stop. You will die if you keep smoking." Her anxious concern provided Mom's incentive. She stopped smoking immediately.

My dad, on the other hand, never quit and seemed proud of his cigarette vice. He died at age 69, measuring his weekly consumption in cartons, not packs. In 2010, I honored his "do not resuscitate" request when I signed the papers removing him from the ventilator. I wonder how much longer would Dad have lived if he'd had a healthier lifestyle.

In 1975, when my parents divorced and our family's life was in turmoil, my aunt and uncle suggested that my then 12-year-old sister, Cyndi, spend the summer with them in Butler, Pennsylvania, near Pittsburgh where my parents grew up. My sister had the opportunity to spend a glorious summer playing with my cousins, attending summer camp, and escaping the drama that was happening at home.

When August arrived, with school soon starting, Mom sent me (then 15) on a Greyhound bus from our home in Glen Burnie, Maryland to Pittsburgh. As usual, I was always expected to care for my sisters. I took a six-hour bus ride up, then in a few days six hours back with my sister. Looking back, I wonder how Mom tolerated my poor attitude. I was focused on me and had no thought of how stressful this must have been for her.

"Stay on the bus until you reach Pittsburgh and you see Uncle Don," she said with a wavering voice that told me she was worried but didn't want me to know.

I was tired of always having to be in charge of my siblings. "Helen to the rescue." This trip was taking me away from my cool new friends, who smoked cigs and gave me hits of their joints. Why did I always have to be the responsible daughter? Out of sight from Mom's watchful eyes, I slinked off the bus and bought my first pack of Marlboros. No one noticed me in the back of the bus, hunched down in the smoking section. I ripped off the cellophane, struck the match and inhaled. The nicotine raced through my body and I raced just as quickly across the aisle to the bathroom to relieve my green stomach. Diligence paid off. By the time I'd made it back to Maryland, I no longer needed to puke. The deed was done: I was hooked on nicotine, my first addiction.

For the next 10 years, I spent too much money and time on a bad habit, averaging two packs of smokes each day. In the 1980s, ashtrays sat on desks and tables at home and at my office. I told myself that the ashtray smoked the majority of those cigarettes. I tried to quit three times. Once, without a cigarette for more than a year, I enjoyed a night out with friends. Everyone around me was puffing away. I caved.

"May I bum a cigarette?" I asked a friend.

She questioned my intentions. "Are you sure?"

"Yes, I'm sure," I retorted in a not-so-nice tone. The nicotine sent shivers through my body. A true addict, I smoked an entire pack of cigarettes the next day.

When I fell in love with my future hubby, life changed in many wonderful ways. Vince did not smoke. When we first started dating, I remember agreeing to his terms.

"Yes, if we end up together, I will quit."

"On a date" meant no smoking in his presence. No problem. I found something that I loved far more than cigarettes: Vince Baratta. For the first time, my emotions controlled my thoughts about my addiction. I began the difficult trial of ridding my body of the need for cigarettes. My struggle didn't end until five years after my first date with Vince. I inhaled my last cigarette on the morning of our wedding in 1984. Poet and writer Brendan Behan said it best: "One is too many and a thousand is not enough."

My obsessive behavior with certain food mirrors my obsession with cigarettes. I overeat pizza. Instead of eating a slice, I want to devour the entire pie. Five years at goal, I finally had the guts to test my control around pizza. I served as host at a church celebration for our Saturday evening service and three Sunday services. Forty pizzas typically arrived for each service, except at nine o'clock morning service, where we served doughnuts. (Thankfully, I have no problem resisting doughnuts.) One Saturday, my pre-planned single slice turned into three pieces of steamy cheesy deliciousness. Still in denial, I added another three slices on Sunday's Live IT© tracker. The good news is that I honestly recorded my intake. Another lesson learned and Behan's words still rang true. One piece was still too many. Going forward, I choose to refrain from pizza altogether.

In the past, when tempting delicacies beckoned me, I gave into their siren call. How on earth do we resist when tasty foods whisper our name? Yes, mine is pizza and, as I mentioned earlier, chips. Yours might be something else.

The seductive thoughts, pulling me in the wrong direction, only have a negative effect when I allow them to influence my choices. *I'm not going to eat this, I'm not going to eat this, I'm not going to eat this* . . . we think to ourselves. And what do we do? We eat it. The enemy has won at this point because we are filled with self-loathing. As Christ's followers, we are asked to practice replacement. We eliminate the bad actions and replace them with good actions. Most sinful actions start with a thought. In this next section, we will learn how to reclaim our thoughts and replace them with God's thoughts, words, Scripture.

Reclaim Your Memory

> *Tell me and I forget, teach me and I may remember, involve me and I learn.*
> –Benjamin Franklin

How and what we think is central to the way we relate and respond to the world. My FP4H Bible study suggests that we memorize a Bible verse each week. On the last day of our sessions, we celebrate anyone who can remember and recite the 10 verses from our study. As the leader, I needed to set the example. At the celebration, standing in front of the group, with all eyes on me, I squeezed the words out of my brain. Remembering Scripture requires intentional time set aside for practice and more practice. My dedication and hard work paid off. I recited the 10 verses.

A brain repository full of Scripture provides an arsenal against the negative thoughts and temptations shooting at us day in and day out. In 2 Corinthians 10:4, we learn, "The weapons we fight with are not the weapons of this world. On the contrary, they have divine power to demolish strongholds." I want to demolish strongholds. My power verse, the one I've repeated more than any other, declares, "No temptation has overtaken you except what is common to mankind. And God is faithful; he will not let you be tempted beyond what you can bear. But when you are tempted, He will also provide a way out so that you can endure it." (1 Corinthians 10:13)

I call on this verse frequently, especially in times when friends, co-workers and family members load the party table with salty chips, velvety dips, glistening brownies wafting their chocolate aroma, trays of cookies positioned in artistic arrays, cakes taking their prominent place with icing begging to be licked, pasta salads oozing with creamy goodness, and the garlic from pizza engulfing my nostrils. Infatuated with the spread, I remind myself why I worked hard ridding my house of unsafe delicacies. The temptation seizes me as my resolve weakens.

Fighting back, I repeat under my breath, "This temptation is common and won't overtake me." Yet the desire is great and self-control is nearly impossible. My gaze scans the room for onlookers, as I repeat the comforting words again. Do people notice that I am talking to myself? Tempting circumstances like this are natural and regular parts of life, frequent, and a probability at any party. Yet I am forever struggling, sending up a 911 call to heaven with each occurrence. "Lord, help. Lord save me."

Still standing at the food table, the overwhelming desire remains as my eyes scan the delectable delights. As the burden of unhealthy options pile up around me. I need a way out. My recall continues: "He won't let me be tempted beyond what I can bear." I remind myself again that God is right there with me and He will help me stand up to the temptation. But it doesn't happen in a split second. My plight continues as I remain at the party and recite, "But when you are tempted, he will also provide a way out so that you can endure it."

Lord, I want success. Help, I beg in silence.

As I glance around, is anyone else at the party stressing over proper quality and quantity of food? Chances are, yes. Is it possible for me to remain calm, make great choices and not retreat? If I'd prepared in advance, I would have chosen my healthy contributions to the feast, like veggies or fruit. If necessary, I flee the area, avoiding the table for the remainder of my stay. One chip, one cookie, one piece of pizza continues to be too many.

Jesus resisted temptation by reciting the words He studied and committed to memory:

"Then Jesus was led by the Spirit into the wilderness to be tempted by the devil. After fasting forty days and forty nights, he was hungry."

The tempter came to him and said, "If you are the Son of God, tell these stones to become bread." Jesus answered, "It is written: 'Man shall not live on bread alone, but on every word that comes from the mouth of God'." (Matthew 4:4)

Jesus endured more temptation and ended the battle quoting Scripture:

"Away from me, Satan! For it is written: 'Worship the Lord your God, and serve him only.' Then the devil left him, and angels came and attended him."

Our temptation-filled lives require that we acknowledge our weaknesses. When we recall the word of God, we admit that we need a savior. With each recollection, our relationship with God strengthens.

Standing at the Scale in Obedience

During my second year into the FP4H program, I hit my first plateau. The scale displayed a 48-pound loss, 49, 48, 47, 49, never hitting the coveted 50 pounds. I hoped for a different result. In the past, I'd quit when the scale remained constant.

"Lord, why so long?" I prayed. "Why won't the scale move? Why am I here? What should I do? Why me? Why now?"

When my kids whined about homework, chores or something not being fair, I told them, "Knock it off." It was only fair that I take my own advice. The plateau stretched on and I griped. One day, coming home on a four-hour drive after visiting my sister, I bent God's ear.

"I'm frustrated, Lord. Why so long, weeks and weeks without a breakthrough? What is the barrier?"

The more I grumbled, the more I reflected on my past failures. I'd never lost more than 50 pounds. I'd always quit when I reached the outstretched plateau. If I regained the weight, what would people say? The more I wrestled with these thoughts, the more fear crept in. Should I settle for 49 pounds?

During the drive I needed a distraction and I flipped on my music player. I entertained myself by warbling a concert with a wide variety of tunes. With no more words left to say to God, I shut up. In FP4H, we memorize a Bible verse each week that is linked to the theme of our Bible study. To help us memorize the verses, they are set to music on CDs that are included with each Bible study. Intended for memorization assistance, the lyrics are repeated four or five times for each song. The memory verse for Deuteronomy 30:11 popped up next on my iPod. The vocalist sang, "Now what I am commanding you today is not too difficult for you or beyond your reach." After the third rendition, I experienced another "2 x 4 moment" as the words sunk in.

Did I believe that God commanded me to lose weight? Aloud in my car, I responded, "Yes." I remembered back to when I started the journey, zapped in my recliner, overwhelmed with an obedient desire to improve my health. The song playing in the car that day declared that the journey is not too difficult. My thoughts argued, It sure feels too difficult. Yet, Scripture states otherwise. Speeding down the highway, I was astounded when I sensed within all of my being that I would reach my healthy weight. From that day forward, my perspective changed forever.

Now convinced that I would lose all the weight and that the 50-pound mark was only a number on the scale, I finally realized how I'd been sabotaging myself. Even though I wanted to push through the barrier, I had been worrying that if I lost the weight, I'd regain it. When the scale at home showed a loss, I would eat more food than needed, so the scale at my meeting would end up with no loss or gain. Embracing this truth after my car ride home that day, I followed the plan as intended and soon crashed through the 50-pound weight loss barrier. When I struggled at 75 and 100 pounds, I returned to my life's verse: "Now what I am commanding you today is not too difficult for you or beyond your reach."

Memorizing Scripture continues to play an important role in my reliance on the Lord. Weekly, I recite my memory verse before stepping on the scale.

With the focus no longer on the scale, God's peace brings everything into correct perspective. I stand at the scale in obedience.

True Measure of Success: Marilyn VanDyk

Marilyn with her husband, Mike, and grandchildren in 2014.

Marilyn VanDyk is the Michigan Networking Leader for First Place 4 Health. Marilyn and her husband, Mike, have three adult children and a multitude of grandchildren. Marilyn is passionate about sharing the wellness of God through His word. Here is her story.

> Our church challenged us to imagine our dream ministry. Mine included studying the Bible and working in the health field. As I prayed and dreamed, I discovered the FP4H materials at a local Christian bookstore. I led two classes the following year.

> One of the secrets to my success is the Live IT© Tracker. Each week, I reviewed my action steps listed on

my tracker and determined whether I had reached the goal or needed an adjustment. I reached my healthy weight within six months.

In 2013, in honor of our 10th year having FP4H at our church, I challenged our class to identify a session goal with the number 10. Some wanted to lose 10 pounds, another who struggled with attendance, set a goal to show up for our meetings 10 out of the 12 weeks. I challenged myself to learn 10 Bible verses during each 12-week session, 40 for the year. I breezed through the challenge during the first session, memorizing 10 verses from the Bible study, "Make Every Day Your Best Day." During the second session, "Walking In Grace", I elicited help from others. My husband quizzed me and shared helpful tips for retention on our walks together. Rhoda, a retired-school teacher and FP4H-er, taught me a unique way of remembering the sequence of the verse location in the Bible. As I emphasized Scripture memory, many in my class began reciting their verses each week. A few joined me and repeated all 10 verses during our victory celebration.

Our third study "Living for Christ" drew all the verses from the book of Ephesians. Adding 10 more verses seemed more daunting and I considered giving up my yearlong goal. When I prayed and asked God for his supernatural power, the verses seemed to jump off the page.

- Ephesians 4:22-24, challenged me to "put off the old self." My old thoughts, "I can't memorize any more verses, it's too hard," were replaced with new thoughts of "Be made new in the attitude of my mind." I changed my thinking in line with Scripture: "All things are possible with God." (Matthew 19:26)

- Ephesians 6:12 shouted to me that my "struggle was not against flesh and blood but was a spiritual battle." My struggle wasn't only in the area of Scripture memory but in many other areas of my life.

- Ephesians 6:18 encouraged me "to pray in the Spirit on all occasions with all kinds of prayers and requests." I asked God for help with reciting the Scripture verses at the upcoming Victory Celebration where I would say from memory for three sessions, 30 verses.

Soon, our fourth session started, called "A Thankful Heart." Daily, I reviewed the previous sessions and added the new session's verses. Humbled and grateful, I thanked God for the blessings and creative ways He wired my brain as I learned new things. God was faithful every step of the way helping me memorize His Word.

When my husband's gall bladder surgery fell on the day of our Victory Celebration, we moved the meeting up one day. The morning of the rescheduled celebration, my husband quizzed me. I struggled with my 40 verses, distracted with the preparations for his surgery, the details for our celebration, and the overwhelming number of verses. I prayed and practiced, still nervous as I arrived to the meeting.

Accepting defeat was not an option. My group encouraged me as we celebrated our victories, yet the room silenced when I stood for my turn. As I finished the first verse from Isaiah 43:18, "Forget the former things; do not dwell on the past", the next eased into my mind: "Therefore do not worry about tomorrow, for tomorrow will worry about itself. Each day has enough trouble of its own" (Matthew 6:34). I felt the presence of the Holy Spirit supernaturally helping me remember. Filled with peace, I continued reciting the 40 verses. Relief and a spirit of praise and gratitude overwhelmed me as I realized God's amazing power working through me.

* * *

Our wellness journey includes battles with our old way of thinking. Once Marilyn internalized Scripture in a new way, the verse became part of her thoughts. Her story is an example of how to change your perspective, read, repeat, remember and, most importantly, recall God's word. Focus on words with truth and embrace the transformation of your mind. Some will say, "I can't memorize. I can't remember. I already have too much in my brain." When we limit ourselves, we fall into a trap of incorrect belief. Don't do that to yourself. Instead be vigilant in your thoughts. The next section will show you how to you replace your thoughts with memorized Scripture.

Reclaim Scripture

Do not conform to the pattern of this world, but be transformed by the renewing of your mind. Then you will be able to test and approve what God's will is—his good, pleasing and perfect will. (Romans 12:2)

What is the best way to be vigilant with our thoughts? I turn to Scripture memorization. It serves as my restoration buffer pad, leveling out thoughts and fears. The following tools helped me to remember Scripture and reclaim reality each time I recited the verses.

1) Art - Draw the Scripture. Act out the verse. Look to the children's ministry where they use verses in interpretive dance or songs with hand motions.

2) Music - Record yourself or someone else singing the verse. Search on the Internet for Scripture recorded to music. Many FP4H studies include Scripture music CDs.

3) Prayer – "Lord help me remember and understand Your Word." Journal your verse; record how the verse applies to your life. Include the verse in your daily prayers. "Lord your Word says, 'You have plans for me and the plans are to prosper me and not to harm me' (Jeremiah 29:11). Lord, I claim that Your plans provide me hope and a future."

4) Redeem Your Time – While commuting or waiting for an appointment, review your Scriptures. Post the Scripture on your mirror or in your closet and recite them during your morning routine. Set your computer password using components of the verse. Recite the verse each time you type your password. Alternatively, use the first letter in each word of a verse for the password; for instance, "For God so loved the world that He gave His only son" (John 3:16) looks like "fgsltwthghosj3:16."

5) Visual - Create flash cards and carry them with you. Write or type the verse multiple times. Recite as you write.

6) Technology - Check your mobile device app store and the Internet. Search on memorize Bible verses.

7) Repetition – Repeat the verse and emphasize a different word each time. Begin by emphasizing the first word in the verse as you say the entire verse aloud. The next time you say the verse, focus on the second word. The third time through, emphasize the third word in the verse. If the verse includes 14 words, repeat the verse 14 times emphasizing a different word.

Relying on God's Word strengthens our mental health as our thoughts conform to His. My thoughts and self-talk transformed from negative and weak into positive and powerful during my plateau. The plateau forced me to identify and remove fear and unbelief. I reclaimed reality and continued my journey, marching onto a healthier weight and better habits. Yet scars extending deep below the surface remained, something that I had yet to address (but will share with you in the coming chapters).

Apprentice with the Master Craftsman

God's Word changed my mind. Embracing the truth, I got serious and busted through the weight loss barrier. What might be your life's verse, the one hitting you upside the head? Take time to memorize it, meditate on it and make it part of your daily life.

Where do you struggle with the temptations and cravings? When we acknowledge our weakness, we recognize our need for a savior. Reciting His word, we shore up our weaknesses, and rely on His strength.

Spend time today waiting expectantly for your deliverance, and journal as you sense His will and power in your life.

Open your Bible and meditate, dwell, internalize and search for a new idea or thought from your heavenly Father. Consider starting with the book of Philippians.

Prayer:

God, forgive me for my thoughts and obstinacy. You are faithful. I love you and want to obey your commands. Look down at me. I ask for your attention to this prayer. I'm praying morning and night (Nehemiah 1:5-6). Change my mind Lord. Help me to sense your presence and hear from you in a new and wonderful way. Encourage and strengthen my resolve in my journey to wellness. Help Lord, I need you today. I pray in Jesus' name. Amen.

Devotions:

Deuteronomy 29:1-15 – Renewal of God's Covenant

Matthew 4:1-11 – The Temptation of Jesus

Deuteronomy 29:16-29 – When We Lived in Egypt

Matthew 4:12-25 – The Beginning of Jesus' Ministry

Deuteronomy 30 – Choose Life or Death

8.
Looking For the Lie

To the Jews who had believed him, Jesus said, "If you hold to my teaching, you are really my disciples. Then you will know the truth, and the truth will set you free."
(John 8:31-32)

The inherent beauty of the floor's wood grain is at its most vulnerable state without a protective finish. Special care must be taken to keep the environment around the floor dry and free from debris. The only one who should walk on the floor at this point is the finisher: our Master Craftsman.

*

My brain sometimes disagrees with the beauty that the mirror reveals. In my mind's eye, up until this point, I still saw the obese person of yesterday. In August 2009, when my weight loss slowed, some might have even said I was done losing weight. In the previous 12-week Bible study session, I'd lost two pounds. I'd been less than 10 pounds away from losing 100 pounds for months and it began to seem unattainable. The lies swirled around in my head as I did my best to focus on the truth.

Lie: You're an utter failure; you've only lost two pounds.

Truth: You've lost and maintained 95 pounds in three years.

Lie: This is as good as it gets. Settle here.

Truth: God was commanding me to lose the weight.
(Deuteronomy 30:11)

Lie: You are too weak.

Truth: I can do all things through God who strengthens me.
(Philippians 4:13)

I realized that I still exhibited behaviors and unhealthy habits during times of stress, emotional upheaval, avoidance, boredom and even in the good times when I celebrated. Some days, I lost the internal battle; other days, I was victorious. It felt as if I was still sabotaging myself, but I didn't know quite why. Something more needed to change and it needed to happen soon.

Emotional Eating

For decades, I found comfort in food. I retreated to the pantry and gazed at the shelves searching for a soothing treat. Instead of asking God for help, I chose food. Convicted when watching the FP4H Emotional Eating DVD, I admitted to myself that I was an emotional eater. FP4H provided the next step through their "Mapping Your Emotional History with Food" program. I uncovered truths about my poor eating habits when I spent time journaling about my emotional history with food. This process helped me to uncover one layer at a time, the triggers and my unhealthy responses, and when and why I ran to food. Once identified, I developed a plan with healthy alternatives. My focus changed from desiring food to seeking God.

I thought that I understood my eating habits when I reviewed my food tracker; however, a deeper look provided the truth that I needed to discover the root cause of emotional eating. I recommend mapping your history with food. To start, find a journal, spiral notebook or any blank page. At the top of separate sheets of paper, write down the different seasons of your life. I wrote: Early Childhood, Childhood, Teen Years, College Years, Marriage

Before Children, Marriage with Children, and Marriage with an Empty Nest. Then find a quiet spot and ask God to show you your relationship with food during each season.

When I asked God to reveal my earliest food memory, I remembered playing in the backyard as a toddler. We lived in a second-floor apartment in an old house. The grey cinder-blocked wall loomed over my head, blocking my view to the neighborhood outside. Alone in the dusty yard, I wanted to play inside with my baby sister. Kathy, born 14 months after my surprise arrival to the world, added complexity to my young mother's life.

"Mommy, I want to play with Kaky," I'd whine.

Mom appeased my pleas for attention with a snack. As soon as I spied the shiny pail in the window with snacks contained inside, I'd race to the wall and look up as Mom lowered my treat down with a string. Mom's reassuring voice told me, "You're okay, Helen. Play a little longer outside while Kathy sleeps. Sit down and eat. Mommy loves you." My emotional attachment to crackers was imbedded in my little girl heart from then on.

I journaled this memory and recognized the deep emotions tied to my cravings for crackers. In the backyard, I experienced boredom, loneliness, fear, abandonment and isolation. Understanding the deep feelings tied to the cracker cravings provided a new freedom and recognition of their false security. I wish I could say that I no longer crave salty-crunchy foods for comfort, but that's not completely true. In fact, the initial weeks of writing this book revealed that the crackers must leave the house until I finished. When I removed them, I sought replacements with chips, graham crackers and pretzels, to name a few. To this day, I approach anything salty and crunchy with care, asking myself, "Am I relying on food instead of my Heavenly Father?"

Ugh.

On one fairly recent occasion, I indulged my craving. I lined a plate with 10 saltines, covered each square with a bit of butter, topped with another saltine, and enjoyed. As I crunched on each one with butter oozing out the sides, I counted the cost. Later I recorded on my tracker, "Cracker Party", or 340 calories between the 20 saltines and two tablespoons of butter. The urge to eat still strong, I found healthy alternatives that had my desired "crunch" factor: veggies and hummus, a crisp apple and air-popped popcorn. Thank goodness I removed the rest of the crackers from my house.

We must prepare for emotional battles that we know will arrive in our lives. When life tests us, our old habit of relying on food for assistance may resurface. The emotional gamut we experience as humans encompasses pride, stress, fear, loneliness, weariness, overwork, anger and much more—even happiness. When are we enjoying ourselves at a party, limiting the feasting may seem harder than resisting ice cream when we are down in the dumps. Who knew parties would be more challenging than crying jags? Society conditions us to join in the fun. I recite verse 1 Corinthians 10:13 often at social gatherings. "No temptation has overtaken you except what is common to mankind. And God is faithful; he will not let you be tempted beyond what you can bear. But when you are tempted, he will also provide a way out so that you can endure it."

What goes on when we are relying on food for comfort? As we stand in front of the pantry searching for something to console us, we must admit that we are emotional eaters. How do we put God first, giving over our will to His? First, with God's assistance, ask why. I mentioned Barb Raveling's book, *I Deserve a Donut,* earlier. The author has also developed an app "I Deserve a Donut." The app steps users through questions uncovering "The lies that make you eat." When we stop and ask why, we flex our "no" muscle and exemplify self-control.

Isaiah the prophet tells us that Jesus came to "proclaim freedom for the prisoners and recovery of sight for the blind, to set the oppressed free" (Isaiah 61:1 and Luke 4:18-21, NIV). When we ask God to reveal our emotional eating triggers, He frees us as we focus in on the truth and see our lives from a new perspective. When we map our emotional history with food, we explore the "when, where, why and how" we overeat.

The new-and-improved me knows that unless it is meal time or snack time, if I'm standing at the refrigerator or pantry door longing to fill my belly, I am in a danger zone. I remind myself, "It's not here." This snaps me out of my desire-driven state. I remember my verses and God's strength returns:

I have the right to do anything, but not everything is beneficial
– 1 Corinthians 6:12

Temptation is common and God is faithful. – 1 Corinthians 10:13

My God will supply me with all my needs. – Philippians 4:19

True Measure of Success: Donnella Looger

Before and after

Donnella Looger, a FP4H leader, passionately helps her group delve into their hearts. Emotional mapping played a significant role in her wellness as she maintains a weight loss of 45 pounds.

FP4H provided the map for me to find my way home. I was a Christian who searched online for a "Christian weight loss program" but I was lost in my perfectionism, self-reliance and self-centeredness. Being fat is hard. I hated shopping in the extended sizes. I hated binging on junk food. I even hated asking God again and again to help me stop the self-sabotage.

I asked God for wisdom according to James 1:5, but ignored the verses that followed: "The one who doubts is like a wave of the sea, blown and tossed by the wind. Such a person is double-minded and unstable in all they do." That described me for many years. The overweight part was obvious and I couldn't hide that, although I spent plenty of time and money trying. But I wore a mask, hiding behind it and presenting to the world that I had my act together.

When I first learned of FP4H, I did not join. I kept gaining weight and deceiving myself. The first thing I thought about every morning when I awoke was my weight, and every day I vowed to make good choices. I'd carefully fix my hair and makeup, always avoiding full-length mirrors. I'm so grateful now that my diet plan didn't work. It was lonely behind that mask. I developed a rash on my face—an allergy to all creams, lotions and make-up. I felt really exposed, fat and ugly. I could no longer just look at my face in the mirror, ignoring the rest of my body, and telling myself, "I'm fine, yep, just fine!" I obviously wasn't.

I finally joined a FP4H ground and soon realized it answered my prayers. When we did the Emotional Mapping, my leader Beverly shared our need to understand "why" before we could even care about the "how." I remember my daddy telling me not to fight the water when he took me out in the Gulf. Even with Daddy holding the inner tube, I'd see those white caps far off and panic. I learned to trust him and float. I stopped fighting and trusted the Lord with my wellness. Growing up near the coast, we had a beach house and I spent lots of time walking on the beach, picking up seashells, building sand castles, and writing in the sand. Every day the tide comes in and goes out, taking those shells, and sand castles and words away, giving a new slate to begin with the next morning.

I've experienced hurricanes in my 63 years, but you know what? Even with the devastation, high winds and storm surges, with each day, the tide ebbs and flows. My lifetime eating plan follows a similar rhythm. Whatever strategies I adopted, they should be ones that I can live with through the weight loss and into maintenance, not some "temporary" and usually radical deprivation.

I lived my life on the sidelines, watching and fantasizing about how I'd become a participant once my appearance was "perfect." I recognize that "lie of the devil" now and exposing it has become my ministry. Our Heavenly Father wants us to be healthy, happy and enjoying all He has provided for us to do, be and have. I urge you to find that rhythm of eating, having your quiet time, and exercising—a rhythm that is pleasurable and healthy that you can enjoy most every day. As that tide comes in and takes some of that sand out to the sea, your new routine will remove the excess pounds along with unnecessary cares and concerns so you can be all that God created you to be.

* * *

Donnella revisits Emotional Mapping each year. I have continued to map my emotions, as well, each time discovering another layer of unhealthy habits. The following are a few more of my discoveries about the earlier seasons in my life and what they taught me about my emotional eating patterns:

Mindless TV Snacking

When I was a little girl in the 1960s, we spent little time in front of the TV. Yet when we were watching TV, we were snacking. As a toddler, I sat on the floor mindlessly consuming pancakes watching *Captain Kangaroo* and *Romper Room*. On Sunday nights, our family huddled in front of the tube with an enormous bowl of popcorn watching *The Wonderful World of Disney* and *The Jackie Gleason Show*. Now, in the evenings when Vince and I wind down in front of the TV, I want to eat. I've found healthy replacements: air-popped popcorn, a pot of tea, crocheting, or some other activity to occupy my hands.

Special Occasions

I was a manager of a large customer service center during the four years I lost my weight. We celebrated someone's birthday at least once per week. I finally realized when losing weight that we should only have birthday cake on our own birthday; but I was the boss and the "right" thing to do was offer me a piece of birthday cake. My staff wasn't trying to sabotage me. They were just being polite. When I started my journey, it took determination to say "no, thank you" as my employees brought me delicacies. My mind tried to trick me: What if I offend them? Surprisingly, no one was offended.

Eventually, as the years wore on and I continued shrinking, people walked in offering me sweet treats, knowing I would decline. As I gained stronger self-control, my "no, thank you" translated to "God, I love you more than this piece of cake."

Today, on special occasions, I treat myself with one or two specialty items. One Mother's Day, our family shared a delicious fried calamari appetizer. You might choose a dessert or the pasta dish you've passed up for months. One Christmas, I baked one batch of chocolate chip cookies for our family to enjoy. On your birthday, enjoy the cake. Otherwise, beware of the frequency of your special occasion splurges—no more than once a month, not once a week, and certainly not daily.

Fail Forward

When we begin to uncover emotional eating habits, we may feel overwhelmed. After all, we've gravitated to food for years, even decades. The enemy of our soul whispers, "You will never change. You've done this forever. Why do you think this time is different?" When we sink into hopelessness, we believe the negative voices, convinced that wellness is for others and we will always "Eat, Eat, EAT."

In his book *Failing Forward,* John Maxwell writes, "Someone who is unable to get over previous hurts and failures is held hostage by the past. The baggage he carries around makes it very difficult for him to move forward." Challenge your mind and fail forward. With each failure, bow down on your knees and ask the Lord for awareness about your mistake.

When I falter, the words from Psalm 139:23-24a serve as my prayer. "Lord, search me and know my heart, test me and know my anxious thoughts, see if there was anything offensive in me, and lead me to the way everlasting." God gently reminds me He is in control. When I confess my failures, I rely more on Him. When we submit to God's divine power, we grow stronger spiritually and hopelessness diminishes into faith.

* * *

In 2008 and 2009, towards the end of my dad's life, I spent time helping him as he struggled with grief and depression following the death of his wife, my stepmother. My stepbrother, Tom, lived in Las Vegas near Dad and would check on him regularly. Every few months, he would raise the flag, asking for help in reviving Dad's spirits. My sisters and I took turns enduring our dad in our homes. He was a tough guest, needing a constant supply of alcohol and cigarettes. His words and actions lacked respect let alone an ability to show love.

In March 2010, during the last two weeks of Dad's life, I stayed with Tom. When I landed, Tom and I drove straight to the courthouse, where we applied for guardianship, as Dad was unable to make decisions for himself. As I walked down the Intensive Care Unit hallway, my left eyelid twitched as I struggled to hold myself together. Already familiar with the hospital scene, Tom smiled and joked with my dad.

Dad yanked at the straps restraining his hands from removing the ventilator tube. The beeping machines overpowered my thoughts, the disinfectant filled my nostrils, and my stomach churned. When the stars reeled in my head, I slid into a chair and put my head between my legs. I wasn't handling the stress as well as I'd hoped.

My stepbrother and I telephoned my sisters to update them on the gravity of Dad's condition. Kathy flew out and joined us a few days later. Cyndi, a stay-at-home mom with three young sons, provided support and prayers over the phone. I am thankful for their support. My husband was an only child. He and I had already walked his parent's death and dying on our own.

At the time, I was only five pounds from reaching my goal. Determined to walk the walk through my dad's illness, I jogged two miles each morning and meditated on Scripture memory verses. At the grocery store, I stocked up on yogurt, whole-grain cereals, breads, salad supplies and fruit. Each morning after my jog, I spent quiet time with God completing my Bible study, reading Scripture and pouring my heart out to the Lord.

In the end, my dad's habits and choices shortened his life. My siblings shared in the decision to remove Dad from the beeping machines. As the oldest, it was my voice telling the doctor, "My father would not want to be on a ventilator for the rest of his life. All of my siblings are in agreement." My hand trembled as I signed the DNR order. Kathy told me years later it's the only time she witnessed me fall apart—emotionally, yes, but I didn't backslide on my healthy habits.

Next up: the grief and the finalizing of Dad's estate. In my past life, I would have eaten myself into a food coma. Instead, I journaled my thanks to God for the disciplines I'd learned over the past four years. I survived a trying time in life and continued to walk in freedom from obesity. God is good all the time. All the time, God is good.

Righteous Replacements

In her book, *Don't Quit Get Fit,* Vicki Heath outlines ways to avoid unhealthy emotional eating.

1) If you can't get food out of your thoughts, drink something satisfying and wait 30 minutes. If the food craving passes, then you weren't really hungry.

2) If you typically snack at specific times of the day or after specific occasions, change your routine.

3) You will tend to eat less if you don't combine eating with another activity, such as watching television.

4) If too many hours pass between meals or snacks, your blood sugar will plummet and you will be more likely to overeat. So eat before you feel famished.

5) Pray through your favorite Scripture verses about food, self-control and your body as a "temple" every day.

6) Identify the locations where you are most likely to eat when you're feeling stressed, and avoid those places on busy or chaotic days. If you usually eat while driving, chew some gum instead or sip a bottle of water or a non-caloric beverage.

7) Keep a daily record of what you eat and review it before each meal. When you're aware of what you've already eaten that day, you may choose to forego that extra helping or sweet. Doing this before you eat will help you form the good habit of thinking before you eat.

8) If you have a pattern of snacking at a certain time of day, keep yourself occupied during that period.

9) Practice eating only when you're sitting down and when you're not otherwise occupied. This will allow you to savor your food and be mindful about what you are eating.

We experience a new freedom when we grasp that our obesity may be rooted in an unhealthy emotional relationship with food. If we want to maintain the weight we worked to lose, we must understand our emotional eating tendencies and learn and practice healthier alternatives.

Apprentice with the Master Craftsman

Food is the drug of choice for emotional eaters. We must learn new ways to cope with life's emotions. Relying on the Lord and embracing his love is crucial for each of us. We must ask ourselves on whose power we are relying. Including God in our struggle provides us with the same power that raised Jesus from the dead. Ask for a filling of God power regularly. Most of us have proven we cannot do this on our own.

Map out your eating history. Start with early childhood, childhood, early teens, teens, life after high school, life on your own, twenties, thirties, forties, married life, divorced life, life with children, life after kids, life with grandkids, life caring for family members, and life grieving. There are many seasons and each brings its own challenges and excuses for unhealthy choices.

As you uncover the why of your emotional eating, take time to talk with a counselor or a trusted friend. It is time to find the core reasons you run to food for comfort.

Prayer:

Heavenly Father, my redeemer, I am determined to live as a free person, no longer shackled to the enemy of my soul or others who have me believe lies. Your amazing love allows me to walk in victory today and forever. Amen.

Devotions:

Isaiah 61:1-11- Freedom for the Captives

Luke 4:1-30 – Tested in the Wilderness

Luke 4: 31-44 – Jesus Amazed People

1 Corinthians 10:1-13 – Common Temptation

1 Corinthians 10:14-33 – Not Everything is Beneficial

Part Three

Buff, Protect and Preserve the Restoration

9.
Starving Sin

To pray is to change. Prayer is the central avenue God uses to transform us. If we are unwilling to change, we will abandon prayer as a noticeable characteristic in our lives.
—Richard Foster

Tremendous time, effort and care have resulted in a smooth new surface to our beloved floor. Now the cleaning begins, as we remove the residual talcum powder with a special cloth made with a tacky surface. Undoubtedly, some dust clings to the surface, and has to be dealt with as part of the overall restoration.

*

In November 2009, I realized that I'd set myself up for failure at the beginning of that year. In early 2009, I'd thought I might break the 100-pounds-lost barrier that year. One little word—"might"—had been at the back of my mind for months. I realized that I didn't really believe that I could achieve this goal. I should have said, "I will." My resolve changed. I stopped my scale-aholic tendency. Instead of checking the scale every day to see what I weighed and then eat based on the scale's display, I weighed in once per week. Instead of inconsistently tracking my food, I tracked with every bite. Instead of exercising three to four days, I upped it to six days a week.

I crossed over into 2010 at the 99-pound lost mark with only 17 pounds to reach my goal. Now, I knew better. Instead of saying, "I might reach my goal", I changed my message to "I will reach my goal" in 2010. So much of me had changed in the past three-and-a-half years. I'd selected a lifetime plan. I'd learned to make healthy food choices and limit my portion sizes. The quantity of food ingested became as important as the quality. I replaced negative thoughts with positive self-talk. I developed daily physical activity disciplines. I substituted bad habits with healthier coping skills. Yet, the last 10 pounds clung to my body, refusing to leave.

My friend Jenn Krogh, a blessed "big loser" herself, has led FP4H groups for more than a decade. She shared that losing those last 10 pounds required perseverance and the need to "starve sin." Similar to the warriors of ancient times, they surrounded an enemy's city preventing the citizens' access to food and water. We, too, need to cut the source that nurtures our unhealthy tendencies. During the battle to lose my last 10 pounds, I learned to starve sin. I'd boast, "I conquered the beast." Then a craving would creep in, my mouth would water, and my mind begged for one more tidbit. We cannot give up what we want most for what we want right now. My eyes raised, my request bold, "Lord, help me." When we persist in resisting the temptation, God smiles and sin dies a slow death on the kitchen floor.

Perseverance transformed my prayer life. At the onset of my journey, I memorized Matthew 21:22: "If you believe, you will receive whatever you ask for in prayer." The more time I spent in prayer, the more I believed. The more I believed, the less I struggled. The less I struggled, the more confident my requests became—a wonderful circle. The following outlines the evolution of my prayer life: how I learned, how others helped, the tools and disciplines I discovered, and the power of God's Word added to prayer.

Learning to Pray

Bold prayers honor God, and God honors bold prayers. –Mark Batterson

The "Lord's Prayer" (Matthew 6:9-13), which I learned in childhood, remains etched in my memory. Under extreme stress, when I desire help the most, I find the familiar words, "Our Father, who art in heaven…" Prayer moves our focus from ourselves towards the Lord Almighty. Daily prayer requires discipline. We must battle our busy schedule. I found strength using the CHAT method, which I learned at church.

> C - Confess. If I am at a loss, I ask, "God, point out my offensive ways." (Psalm 139:24)
>
> H - Honor. I praise God for who He is. I might say, "Lord you are Father, Son, and Holy Spirit. You are my savior, my all."
>
> A - Ask. Where do I need help? "Daddy God, help my choices honor you when I speak, eat and move my body."
>
> T - Thank. "Thank you for my salvation, my husband, my sons, my health, my family, my friends and my church. Thank you for the multitude of blessings in my life."

I added CHAT as a recurring appointment in my online calendar at seven o'clock every morning and at 10:30 each evening. When the fog clears from my brain in the morning, I spend my first waking moments chatting with God. If I forget, the first glance at my phone reminds me of my appointment with my Heavenly Father. As the day ends and I fall asleep, I chat with God.

When I start my day in conversation with the Lord, I find myself relying on His advice throughout the day. With each request, I hand over the reins seeking His direction. Small or big, my requests often require a change in my situation.

"Father, the traffic slows me down. Help me arrive on time."

"Daddy God, help me exercise today. My time and desire are limited."

"Help, Help, Help! The chips are calling my name!"

"Holy Spirit, give me the right words for my response."

Author Richard J. Foster writes in his book *Celebration of Discipline:* "To pray is to change. Prayer is the central avenue God uses to transform us. If we are unwilling to change, we will abandon prayer as a noticeable characteristic of our lives." When we struggle with daily prayer, ask the Lord for help. He will reveal our unwillingness for change or the poor habit we refuse to acknowledge. Then request, "Lord, change my heart." Remember, if you want God to do something new in your life, you must be willing to do something new, as well.

Prayer Partners

When we spend time with God, praying for each other, we strengthen our spiritual muscles together. At first, I felt selfish when I asked for prayer. Yet I would ask others for their prayer needs and spend time each week praying for their requests. In FP4H, I learned to write out a personal prayer request detailing the behaviors that I needed to add, change or remove from my lifestyle. Mine often reads:

"Help me fill out my food tracker honestly and completely. Help me exercise five times a week. I am traveling and need help with food choices."

My partners expressed weariness with the same requests for help week after week. I shared with them, "I need the Lord to change my mind about tracking and exercise. Change my 'need to' into a 'want to.' Please pray for me."

Even today, when I receive texts or emails from my partners, I am encouraged. I know, without a doubt, that prayers were requested to the Almighty for me. I am thankful for all who have prayed for me on my journey, and continue to do so.

When we share our needs with others, we provide a transparent façade to our battle plan. One of the FP4H groups that I helped to start in 2010 at Crossroads Church meets on the east side of the city in Pittsburgh. Jacki Lynn Baynks assumed leadership of the group in 2012 so I could take on other responsibilities in the FP4H ministry. I beamed when I read Jacki Lynn's account of the group's perseverance, supporting and praying for each other on their wellness journey.

Friends Don't Let Friends Stay Overweight

Comfortable and safe, together we practice the FP4H four-sided balanced living formula focusing first on Christ. We encourage each other when we love with our HEART. When we study the Bible we love with our SOUL side, which seems the easiest for our group to accomplish. Toughest, the BODY side, holding each other accountable when our food choices or lack of physical activity affects our weight or the MIND side pressing on, challenging each other to learn our memory verses. This session, we brainstormed a new motto: "Friends don't let friends stay overweight." Our sense of empowerment grew as we listed our individual accountability needs.

- One member, Lisa, shared: "I must remain alert and aware of my emotional buttons leading me to overeat." She counters her emotions with a regular walk.

- Liz shared that success comes when she pre-prepares her meals paying close attention to the calories.

- Marian identified her physical weakness with mindless eating, a possible result of her medication. Tracking helps her with accurate measurement of the amounts instead of the inaccurate estimation when she doesn't track.

- Jacki Lynn identified salt as a downfall. "When I eat salty foods, I need to drink larger quantities of water. Tracking provides me the information I need to remain within a healthy sodium limit and remain hydrated."

In 2014, Jacki Lynn moved from Pittsburgh and the group stopped meeting. After many months and the inevitable rising weights on the scale, several group members started attending another FP4H group 40 minutes from their homes. Eventually, a new leader emerged and the group returned to the east side of the city. Their wellness journey continued together and to this day, they have not stopped.

In 2011, I formed a team of friends and family who pray for me. A friend coordinates my team and sends me reminders for my requests. Monthly, I send a letter sharing praises and specific requests based on my challenges, my schedule and my life overall. Their time in prayer on my behalf created an added level of accountability. The completion of this book proves the effectiveness of their prayers.

Prayer Wheel

In *The Hour That Changes the World,* author Dick Eastman divides an hour into 12 periods of five minutes each, specifically for the use of prayer. At first, I could not comprehend praying for an hour. I started with 12 minutes, one minute for each section. My attitude changed when I added the Prayer Wheel to my exercise routine. When I walked, I changed prompts at two-minute increments. When I started running, I changed at a 10th and increased to a quarter mile. I printed the wheel and carried it with me in a plastic baggie. I eventually laminated it and carry it tucked in my purse. Now etched in my memory, I pray when I swim laps, changing prompts at each lap.

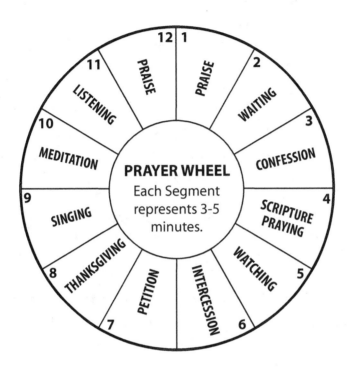

The following is my interpretation of the Prayer Wheel:

Praise: Acknowledge God for who He is. Exalt Him with your words. I name God using the ABCs: Almighty, Beautiful, Counselor and so on until "Z."

Waiting: God always with us, surrender your time and wait with hope. I quiet myself, ready with expectation.

Confession: Ask for forgiveness of sins. Time flies in this section. I ask, "Reveal my offensive ways, oh Lord."

Scripture Praying: Remind the Lord of the promise His word

provides. I reword Scripture or my memory verses as a prayer. "Lord I believe I will receive whatever I ask for in prayer."

Watching: Tell God where you find Him at work in your life, in your family, in the world. I share my awe. "You amaze me. You transformed this couch potato into someone who enjoys exercise."

Intersession: Share with Him about the needs and concerns of others. I start with my husband, my sons, their future wives, extended family and friends. Then I focus on my leaders, the people I lead, and those I serve beside in ministry.

Petition: Identify the needs for yourself. Once I exhaust my laundry list, I lapse into silence and ask the Lord for His perspective on my needs.

Thanksgiving: Express appreciation for the blessings in your life. I thank Him for my salvation, marriage, family, health, church, friends and our freedoms in the United States.

Singing: Worship the Lord with song. I wonder what my neighbors think of "Hallelujah Helen" when they see me running and singing at the top of my lungs!

Meditation: Reflect on a matter more closely. Oftentimes, by this step in my prayer wheel, a theme has emerged. In the past, I've meditated on obedience, love, discipline, joy, an action step and even a chapter in this book.

Listening: Notice and pay attention with a God centered focus. Finally, I am quiet in my heart, in my mind and in my soul. I expect His presence when I listen. I am excited. I am ready.

Praise: Spend time in the presence of the Lord, King of Kings. Praise Him.

I look forward to the prayer wheel. We enjoy a BOGO (buy one, get one free) when we spend time in prayer while exercising. We increase both physical and spiritual strength at the same time.

Fasting

Beware in your prayer, above everything, of limiting God, not only by unbelief, but by fancying that you know what He can do. —Andrew Murray

At the beginning of my weight loss journey, I said boldly to my class, "I will never give up half-and-half." Although coffee seemed a necessary requirement for daily survival, the added condiments racked up calories. In 2008, my pastor challenged us, "Give up a luxury for 40 days." The 40 days has spiritual significance as it symbolizes the temptation of Christ following his time spent in the desert denying himself (Matthew 4:1-11).

My church's focus provided the holy motivation I needed as others joined in "giving up" something, too. I gave up my precious four cups a day of caffeinated goodness. No coincidence, around the same time, I learned that consuming low-fat dairy products helps with weight loss when I read an article written by Kathleen Zehlman titled, "Is Calcium the New Magic Bullet?" When the 40 days ended, I savored my cup of coffee with one-half cup of steamed skim milk instead of half-and-half. The Lord blessed me with a bonus. I cut the fat from my diet and increased my dairy intake.

Over the course of my wellness journey, I experienced more self-control after I abstained from something for an extended period of time.

- In 2009, I gave up alcohol for the summer, hit my 100-pound-lost threshold and recognized that alcohol lessens my self-control.

- In 2011, I improved my blood pressure when I removed caffeine for the last time. Today, I enjoy a cup of decaffeinated coffee periodically with skim milk, of course. I'm shameful when I brag of my consistent normal pressures. After the initial withdrawal, my body no longer requires the caffeine.

- In 2012, I recognized my non-existent Sabbath. Weekly, I unplug from email with a 24-hour fast from my laptop.

- In 2014, as I've already shared, I removed crackers from the house when I started writing this book. Crackers are still on the "I can never give up" list. I hope to have self-control with crackers someday but I know myself well enough to say that today is not that day.

- In 2016 and 2017, my accountability partner and I started the year with a 21-day Ultimate Daniel Fast based on the book of the same name by Kristen Feola. We eliminated all animal products, sweeteners, leavened breads, refined or processed foods and solid fats. Water was our only beverage. I welcomed meats and breads when I broke my fast. The long-term result is that I consume a minimal amount of sugar and prefer less processed foods.

Abstinence and fasting helped me to understand hunger—physically and spiritually. When my mind and body yearn for the off-limits item, in silence I assert, "God, I want You." With each denial, my spiritual life deepens and my self-control strengthens. Consider denying yourself something for 40 days. Pray and ask God to reveal the food or habit you will "never" give up. Give up and give God the glory.

Demolishing Strongholds

I have found that there are three stages in every great work of God: first it is impossible, then it is difficult, then it is done. —Missionary J. Hudson Taylor

In 2013, I discovered Bible teacher Beth Moore's book, *Praying God's Word: Breaking Free from Spiritual Strongholds.* She points out that the world does not understand the war we battle as those struggling with overweight and obesity. She explains the meaning of "strongholds" by quoting 2 Corinthians 10:3-5:

> Basically, a stronghold is any argument or pretension that "sets itself up against the knowledge of God." The wording in the King James Version draws a clearer image of a stronghold: ". . . every high thing that exalteth itself against the knowledge of God." A stronghold is anything that exalts itself in our minds, "pretending" to be bigger or more powerful than our God.

I find that hope fills our souls as we fight with divinely powered weapons and demolish strongholds. In Ephesians 6:17-18, Paul identified the offensive weapon: the sword of the Spirit as the Word of God. When I pray through God's word, I believe that He desires my deliverance and everyone else's from the strongholds in our lives. The eighth chapter of Moore's book, "Overcoming Food-Related Strongholds", ministered to my food addictions. The next chapters dealt with overcoming pride, then un-forgiveness, and overcoming the enemy. New courage and strength overflowed as the strongholds dissolved from their tight grip on my thoughts when I prayed with God's words. I moved from hopeless to hope filled as God answered my prayers.

Transformed, I prepared for battle and downloaded the Kindle version of *Praying God's Word.* When people shared their stories with me, I asked the Lord for wisdom as their cries for help penetrated my soul. Some battle depression, others grief, unbelief, addiction, rejection or even sexual strongholds. If I sensed prayer was the best course of action, I asked permission: "May I pray with you?" Based on the circumstance, with confidence, I turned to the corresponding chapter in *Praying God's Word*. As we prayed together, God's supernatural power would take over. I've witnessed healing both emotional and physical as strongholds dissolved. The Word of God creates a new path in our mind and transforms our thoughts.

Beware that when we pray God's Word over another person, we are at war with the enemy. We must battle if we plan to win the war. Pray then read Scripture. Pray then read Scripture. Repeat as many times as necessary. Think of yourself as a surgeon, cutting away the stronghold wielding a scalpel, God's mighty word.

The Power of Prayer

In July 2010, my thumb developed a nasty infection, requiring a doctor's visit. I squeezed the appointment in during my lunch with one of the covering physicians. The nurse called for me in the waiting room and I followed her down the hall. The scale, our first stop, no longer threatened me. The nurse looked up from her clipboard when I shouted, "Yahoo!" The scale displayed my long-awaited goal, 158. I skipped down the hall and entered the examination room.

She closed the door and inquired, "What's going on?"

"I reached my weight loss goal!" I said, a little too loud.

The nurse, smiled and nodded, "That's nice."

When the thermometer she thrust in my mouth beeped, she commented, "One-hundred degrees. Why are you here today?"

I knew she had no idea that this was a special day for me. Still, I was miffed that she didn't acknowledge the significance. Who cares about my thumb? Inside my head, I celebrated. *I reached my goal. I reached my goal. I reached my goal!* She gathered the information she needed, wrote a few things on the chart, and walked out the door.

The examination table crinkled as I did a happy dance. After a few minutes, the doctor entered the room holding my chart. He questioned me about my thumb then wrote a prescription for an antibiotic.

"I want you back here in two weeks for a follow-up," he instructed. Perched on the stool, looking over the chart, he asked, "What's this about reaching your goal?"

I gave him a short run down of the last four years. He looked back at the chart. "The highest weight I find is 274 pounds," he commented. "By my calculation, you lost a total of 116 pounds. You need to claim all of it as weight loss."

"Absolutely," I responded.

I reached my goal. My prayers answered. Hallelujah. My praises polished, my soul now shining with God's glory. Yet, little did I know the hardest work was yet to come.

Apprentice with the Master Craftsman

Transformation does not happen in our strength or power. What struggles do you battle in your own power that can only be accomplished through God's power?

"Daily prayer requires discipline." Document your needs as if you were a physician. Summarize the condition. List the root causes of the situation. Write out a prescription with prayer and include God's word as the medicine.

Prayer:

Lord, forgive me for the times I refrain from bringing my needs to you. You are Creator, Provider, Healer, Redeemer, Judge, Defender and much more. Help me live a life of prayer spending daily time with You. Thank you for your love and compassion. You never turn me away. Your love and patience overwhelm me. Amen.

Devotions:

Matthew 21:1-22 – Blessed is He

Matthew 21:23-46 – Jesus' Authority Questioned

2 Corinthians 10 – Demolish Arguments

2 Corinthians 11:1-15 – False Teachers

2 Corinthians 11:16-30 – Show My Weakness

10.
The Final Top Coat

Two are better than one, because they have a good return for their labor: If either of them falls down, one can help the other up. But pity anyone who falls and has no one to help them up.

(Ecclesiastes 4:9-10 NIV)

Three thin coats of polyurethane are better than two thick coats. Apply the finish with swift overlapping strokes in a single back-and-forth motion. The smoother the floors are buffed between coats, the smoother the final finish. Dust and clean the surface with a tack cloth before adding a new layer. Stand back and admire the flawless final coat.

*

It was 2010. I celebrated the new me being reflected in the mirror. Yet, when I closed my eyes, the obese Helen still appeared, even four years after reaching my goal. I wondered, "How long before I reflect the new me in my new mind?" I revisited the same questions that I answered when I started my journey.

WHAT: Initially, I desired weight loss. Now I treasured sustained health and wellness for lifetime.

WHY: Before, I longed to look great, feel great and enjoy a great life.

Now I choose wellness to serve God for as long as He has me on earth.

WILL YOU: For decades, I responded, "No, I won't. I can't. I've already tried." Then I recognized God's unimaginable love for me and responded "yes" when prompted to embrace my body as the temple of His Holy Spirit.

HOW: I surrendered to God's supernatural power. I sacrificed my time and desires as I changed to a healthier lifestyle one day and one pound at a time. I relied on help and prayers from others. Now as the journey continues, I still need help.

A New Level of Accountability

A week after I reached my healthy weight of 158 pounds, I flew to Houston, Texas to attend my first FP4H Summit Conference. Each year, FP4H hosts this two-day event with success stories, breakout sessions on leadership, nutrition, spiritual growth, and a keynote speaker to inspire us. I marveled at the vast size of the facilities at Houston's First Baptist Church. I'd never been in a mega-church before. It resembled a community college and I needed a map to find my way around the campus. Even though I attended one of the largest churches in Pittsburgh, it was dwarfed by this 4,000-seat worship center.

Houston First Baptist Church originated First Place 4 Health for their congregation in 1981. Over the years, the ministry spread to other churches, denominations and eventually became a separate nonprofit ministry. I thanked God for the many people who have served the ministry over the years. Star-struck, I met leaders and teachers I'd watched on the DVDs and read about in books. The speakers challenged my perspective:

- Vicki Heath, then associate director, shared: "If you do not quit, you will succeed."

- Becky Turner, emcee and breakout session speaker said: "Say 'no' so you can say 'yes' to a greater yes."

- Joyce Ainsworth, networking leader and breakout session speaker, shared: "Learn to choose well. Don't focus on good and bad, but the best choice."

- Carole Lewis, then the national director added: "We are better together. The hard work of change is easier with a friend."

The fellowship filled my soul. I met others who would encourage and sustain me on my new maintenance journey. I sat next to Jennifer Krogh from Kewaunee, Wisconsin. We discovered many similarities in our lives: mothers of two sons, long lasting marriages, spouses who loved us regardless of our physical sizes, each of us memorized Psalm 139, and both blessed "big losers." Jenn had maintained a 165-pound loss for more than four years. I'd hit my 116 pounds lost only days before.

As the summit wrapped up, Carole Lewis challenged everyone: "Find an accountability partner before you leave." Convinced that God ordained our chance meeting, Jenn and I exchanged contact information and scheduled a follow-up video-conference. During our first meeting, we set the parameters for the future. We would meet one hour every two weeks and end each meeting with prayer. Jenn planned to sit for the American Council on Exercise (ACE) certification for Personal Fitness Trainer in 2011. She suggested that I help her stay on track with her study schedule. I needed her help to navigate the next phase in my restoration: maintaining my healthy weight.

Each time we talked and shared intimate details of our lives, our friendship deepened. We laughed, we cried and we challenged each other all within an hour marked by the grandfather clock in Jenn's study. If we ran over our time, the bongs of the clock forced us to pause and wait for the quiet ticking to return.

A few months into our meetings, Jenn shared the challenge of fitting in the studying for her exam. She hinted that the ACE exam deadline was approaching and she wasn't sure she would pass. She squirmed as I raised my eyebrow and said, "You gave me a job when we started. What do you need from me to help you?" She determined studying one hour per day would allow her to absorb the material. I requested a daily report via text.

Each day when the text arrived, I prayed for her and responded with an encouraging text: "Way to go." "You can do this." "Keep going." Or, "Praise the Lord." Jenn took the exam on the last possible day during snowy and hazardous conditions. She drove 45 minutes to the testing site near Green Bay, Wisconsin. I prayed for her through the entire commute then the three hours during the exam. We celebrated via text when she left the testing site with her ACE certification. Another huge win!

Jenn blessed me with the same scrutiny I provided her for her ACE exam. Years later, Jenn and I are in regular contact via text, email, telephone and periodically through video-conference. The Lord knew I needed someone who had already traveled the path and navigated maintenance with success. She was and continues to be a big answer to my prayers. Here is Jenn's story.

True Measure of Success: Jenn Krogh

Before and after

I was a chubby child. During puberty, when appearance and approval were of critical importance, I gained 70 pounds over three years. My self-esteem plummeted. I had an ongoing battle in my mind over food and my weight. A part of me desired a thin body, yet the pull of food was greater. When I overate, I hated myself until my tummy ache subsided and it would start over again.

At 19, I discovered "diet doctors" who prescribed amphetamines. I lost weight with no difficulty. I had no appetite and was tense, unable to sleep. I ignored the health risk of damage to my body for the sake of losing weight. When I stopped taking the pills, my appetite resumed, and I regained the 58 pounds I'd lost. During this time, I met and married my husband and we became eating buddies, and we both gained additional weight.

Next, I purchased processed food through the commercial diet plan. I followed the plan and lost 50 pounds in a short period. Since the food was expensive, I quit. My old habits put me right back where I started, and then some. I quit smoking a few years later and added another 40 pounds. I lived in elastic-waist pants and spent my days obsessing about food and being thin. When our first child was a few months old, I weighed in at 300 pounds.

I began a Christian weight management program in 1993, and had intended to keep it a secret. After multiple failures in losing weight, only to regain it, I didn't want anyone to know, even though it was different this time. God was a part of this journey and I did have hope, but not enough to have an audience. The Lord put me in the hot seat of leadership right off the bat. He knew I needed the accountability, and that I wouldn't quit when the going got tough. It did get tough in the second year—with a loss of seven pounds. The first year I lost 80 pounds and it almost seemed easy. The weight came off week after week; the numbers on the scale dropped and so did my clothing size. The second year was discouraging, but the commitment to my group brought me back each Monday night.

The physical changes have been nothing short of a miracle and I'm grateful. My total weight loss is 165 pounds from my heaviest (many years ago) to my current weight, which is less than when I was in the seventh grade. God has healed me emotionally, challenged me mentally and continues to grow me spiritually. Fulfillment comes from watching individuals learn to care for their bodies and enjoy it, too. I need health-focused community. I don't see that as being weak or needy. Accountability is for good, not to control or dominate.

Sometimes I imagine my life as if I decided to stay in my elastic-waist pants and not accept responsibility for my weight. Obviously, my physical appearance changed, but what about my health? Diabetes? Heart disease? Mobility limitations? I gained so much by losing. I cannot state the value of my experiences because I was fit enough, the relationships I formed over the years, which might not exist, or how God over and over gave me His strength. A quote from Mary Ann Evans, known by her pen name George Eliot, hangs on my office wall: "It's never too late to be who you might have been." I am eternally grateful for God's plan for me. I am also grateful for the support and encouragement provided through the many individuals along my journey. A few who came alongside are true kindred spirits. In those special relationships, a connection brings an understanding. It's rare when we identify with one another. When I met Helen and discovered we were both in the 100-plus pounds lost club, we sensed the divine appointment. Accountability gives strength for the journey, Jesus with skin on and the privilege to share what God's doing in and through our lives.

* * *

Jenn continues as a rock in my life and I'm thankful for her special way. She sends me adorable cards. When she senses that I'm in a danger zone, she requests a report on my spiritual, mental, emotional and physical state. When my weight is up, I text a picture of my toes on the scale every week. If I'm struggling with tracking accuracy, I send her a copy of my tracker.

Iron Sharpens Iron

As iron sharpens iron, so a friend sharpens a friend. (Proverbs 27:17 NLT)

Each of us need people in our lives who will spur us onto meet our goals, ask us tough questions when we're not experiencing success, wait for our responses, challenge us when we might be lying to ourselves, and cheer us on when we discover the steps to success. Since 2001, I've been in multiple small groups filled with people striving for a Christ-filled life. Group members cheered me on spiritually, helped me apply the weekend message, and stretched me as we served others together. When I became a small group leader in 2002, I had multiple coaches who encouraged, challenged and inspired me. In 2006, when I started the FP4H ministry at my church, I met privately with my coach Sue Neeley. Sipping tea, I sighed, "I'm in over my head."

Sue paused before she responded. "I'm not sure how to start a ministry, either. What I am sure of is that God has a plan. I'll help you discover His plan."

Sue's encouragement and prayer elevated my spirits and confidence. We've spent many holy moments in prayer together seeking next steps for the ministries I've led. She prayed with me. She prayed for me. She still prays for me. When blessings abounding, I couldn't wait to phone Sue and share the answered prayers. Sue started out as my spiritual mentor. Ten years later, she is my spiritual sister forever.

I became a coach myself when the FP4H ministry blossomed. I was excited to encourage others. I coordinated coaching sessions where leaders shared struggles and successes, and prayed for each other. Some of the holiest of prayers I've experienced were with leaders listening and asking the Lord for direction for each other.

I've also experienced spiritual change through a one-on-one Life Change Group (LCG), (cmaresources.org) two or three individuals who meet weekly. It's difficult to hide when we're face to face asking each other about our spiritual condition. The LCG meeting lasts one hour. My partner and I agree to read the same Bible passages throughout the week on our own. During our meetings, we share what we've learned about Jesus from reading the Bible. Then we review what I call the "scary questions", which address our character in Christ. Out of the 11 questions, number six is the hardest for me: "Have you used anything or done anything that you know you should not be doing this week?"

We all struggle with some type of inappropriate attraction hampering our relationship with God. I most often confess my food choices or lack of completing my tracker. The planned 60 minutes quickly tick away. We end with prayer for our friends and family who need Jesus and prayer for each other. LCGs might last six weeks, six months or even up to a year.

In 2008, I met with a member from my small group for my first LCG. We both wanted to read through the Bible in a year. We did. Next, a woman I met through our sons' marching band events joined me. Reading the Bible was a new experience for her. Our friendship cemented forever when she gave her life to Christ on my birthday months after we started meeting. So far, I've been involved in LCGs with six different people who became my closest friends in our quest to be more like Christ. Once each ended, I pray for another person to join me in a new LCG. The discipleship cycle continues.

Coming Clean With the SOAP System

Another method helped me spend time with the ultimate accountability partner, Jesus. In his book the *Divine Mentor*, Wayne Cordeiro developed the "SOAP" system for documenting and processing Scripture readings. I've filled my journals with SOAP since 2008.

S – Scripture, identify a verse in the Scripture reading

O – Observation, notice and record the details

A – Application, identify an action for ourselves

P - Write a prayer requesting courage to act on the application

When we SOAP each day in God's Word, we are clearing the way for our transformation. Simply say "yes" to all that Jesus has for you.

Accountability Practices

Here are some general best practices to use when choosing your accountability partner.

- Confidentiality counts. How can you share your deepest needs if you are not in a safe environment?

- Challenge versus condemn. We receive enough condemnation from the enemy. Recognize the difference. Love one another.

- Meet in private, free from distraction. We need a place for honest and transparent conversation, where tears might flow and laughter resonates.

- Choose someone of your same gender. If you are married, safeguard your relationship with your spouse.

- Spouses play a different role. Yes, read Scripture with your spouse, pray together, encourage one another and even challenge each other.

They are not your accountability partner.

If you need someone to fill the role of accountability partner, take comfort. God already knows the person or persons. Start with prayer. Jesus said, "...I tell you, whatever you ask for in prayer, believe that you have received it, and it will be yours" (Mark 11:24). We need people who speak truth, point us in the right direction, and steady us when our resolve weakens. Each accountability relationship ignites collaboration toward shared progress and accomplishment, and adds a layer of protection against life's never-ending pitfalls.

Apprentice with the Master Craftsman

WHAT do you want for your life? What is your dream?

WHY do you want a healthy life? Why or why not?

WILL you do what is needed?

WHO is speaking truth into your life?

Prayer:

Help me Lord, when my heart seeks shelter and protection from the pitfalls on my journey. Thank You for hearing me and responding with your mighty presence. Help me share my needs with others who might encourage me. Give me confidence to ask for accountability from others. Amen.

Devotions:

Ephesians 1 – Spiritual Blessings

Ephesians 2 – By Grace You are Saved

Ephesians 3 – God's Marvelous Plan

Ephesians 4 – Unity and Maturity

Ephesians 5 – Always Give Thanks

11.
Divine Protection

Finally, brothers and sisters, rejoice! Strive for full restoration, encourage one another, be of one mind, live in peace. And the God of love and peace will be with you.
(2 Corinthians 13:11 NIV)

Applying felt protectors to the furniture legs prevents scratches and dents to your new gleaming surface. Never drag or push heavy objects over your hardwood floors. Treat them with loving care. A vacuum cleaner and dust mop are your best friends when it comes to daily maintenance. Step back and admire your gleaming accomplishment.

*

My stepmother, Jene, demanded an immaculate house. In 1975, when we moved in with her and my Dad, I was faced with her clean house obsession. The five teens (two stepbrothers, two sisters and me) rotated our daily cleaning assignment each week: kitchen, bathroom, vacuum, trash or dust. Vacuuming and dusting every surface each day seemed like a big waste of my time.

Each night, when Jene arrived from work, she'd inspect our assignments. If we didn't vacuum in straight lines, she criticized our ability to focus. If someone used the bathroom after it had been cleaned, she scowled at the water spots on the spigot. One time, she chased my stepbrother around the house, screaming and calling him lazy and worthless when he failed to do his chores. I found it easier to have my job completed than to experience her wrath.

When I returned to work outside the home after the birth of my first son, I struggled with the cobwebs appearing in the corners of my house. My mother-in-law, bless her heart, convinced my husband that I needed a cleaning lady. The best money I'd ever spent paid someone to professionally clean and dust my house every two weeks.

Jene passed away a few years before my father died in 2009. If she were still alive, she'd be mortified at my house, even though it's fairly clean. Her obsession left an impact. To this day, each night before bed, I clean the kitchen and run the dishwasher. In the morning, I unload the dishwasher and prepare for the day's dirty dish brigade. How and why did I struggle to find time to care for myself when I was obsessed with a clean kitchen?

Whole person wellness requires a similar daily focus of nutritious food choices, physical activity, adequate rest, and quiet time with God. Maybe if I could view self-care as dirty dishes, it would be easier. Load, clean, put away. Load, clean, put away. Eat, move, rest in God. Eat, move, rest in God.

The Transformed Attitude

I surprised my friends and family when my healthy lifestyle commitment persisted for longer than a few months into my weight loss journey. As I've mentioned several times already, I'd quit countless times before. So let's review what I've presented in these chapters: Why was this time different?

The Lord transformed my attitude in four areas.

I adopted a new spiritual attitude when I recognized my body was the temple of the Holy Spirit. My physical situation prevented me from fulfilling the purpose God planned for my life. I spent more time than I am proud of arguing with God about the decades of failed weight loss attempts. I was 46 when I finally agreed to start a First Place 4 Health group at my church. I learned a new way to feed by body and my soul. Thank you Lord for the transformation.

I adopted a new attitude about physical activity when I recognized healthy people exercise every day. In the past, I dreaded exertion and spent most of my time in a chair or on the couch. Today, biking, hiking, swimming, dancing and group fitness fill my days. I've crossed off bucket list items—from stand-up paddle boarding to parasailing. Thank you Lord for transformation.

I adopted a new attitude in my thoughts. Memorized Scripture stored in my brain provides resistance when tempting thoughts threaten my resolve. I recall my power verse, when faced with temptation: "No temptation has overtaken you except what is common to mankind. And God is faithful; he will not let you be tempted beyond what you can bear. But when you are tempted, he will also provide a way out so that you can endure it" (1 Corinthians 10:13 NIV). Each time I recall a Scripture, God's powerful Spirit surges through me. I cherish the self-control I sense from the Holy Spirit. Thank you Lord for transformation.

I adopted a new attitude when I mapped my emotions and uncovered the unhealthy patterns in my life. When life was in turmoil, my previous first response was to stand in the pantry searching for food to numb the discord. I learned that food is not my friend or comforter. Food is fuel. My Live IT© Tracker from FP4H provides truth, energy in (food) and energy out (activity). Thank you Lord for transformation.

Protect Your Attitude With God's Armor

An important key to maintaining a transformed attitude is an extra level of protection. My coach, Sue Neeley, protects herself each day, while in the shower, reciting from memory the words tailored from the Bible, found in Chapter Six in the book of Ephesians titled the "Armor of God" (Ephesians 6:10-18).

The Armor of God

Lord, gird me up with Your Truth, so I don't trip on my own thinking. Cover my heart with your breastplate of righteousness, for I have no righteousness of my own. Shod my feet with the gospel of peace, that I may walk prepared and protected in this world, sharing the Peace of the Gospel. Place on my head the helmet of my salvation. Help me to remember that I am in You and You are in me. Give me the mind of Christ, that I may know your will and be obedient to it. Let nothing come into my mind or out of my mouth that does not bring You honor and glory. I take up in my left hand, the shield of faith soaked in the living water to ward off the fiery darts and arrows of the enemy. I take up in my right hand, the sword of the Spirit Your Word, which is made meaningful to my heart through your Holy Spirit. In this armor I stand and pray, asking for a hedge of protection physically, spiritually, mentally, and emotionally. Help me Lord, to reflect on your love, be alert and unfailingly pray for your kingdom. Fill me Lord, this day, with your Holy Spirit. Amen.

Our first protective layer recognizes God's truth. It is not about us. We wake up each morning because of God. The second protective layer covers our heart. We have no righteousness of our own. We all fall short. We are right with God only because of Jesus.

The gospel of peace is our third layer. The verse says to "shod your feet with the gospel of peace." We put on socks and shoes to protect our feet and help us move faster across the prickly earth. We stand firm in the good news of Jesus. We can walk, run, climb and even skip with the good news of Jesus' peace. The gospel of peace is a perfect fit for our feet as we stand firm in Jesus' love. What a wonderful protective layer.

The fourth layer goes on our head, the helmet of salvation. Back in the Roman soldiers' day, the sturdy helmets were made of thick leather covered with metal. The helmet protected the head from heavy double-sided swords. In today's world, the whispers we hear in our head from the enemy could be double-sided lies. The truth of salvation through Christ sets us free (John 8:31-32). Our transformed attitude becomes like Christ and allows us to identify the truth from the lies (Romans 12:2). It's transformation and protection all in one piece of armor.

The shield of faith soaked in the living water provides the last layer and protects against the fiery darts of the enemy. The darts come in all different sizes and shapes. Each is tailored for our unique weaknesses. The Roman soldier's shields where heavy, rectangular, the size of the soldier. Before battle, they soaked their shields in the river then hauled their shields to the battlefield, soaked and dripping. Their faith that the shield would protect them emboldened them to fight longer. We, too, must hold our shield of faith soaked with living water. Jesus said in John 7:38, "Whoever believes in me…rivers of living water will flow from within them."

The last item in the armor is an offensive weapon, the Word of God. 2 Corinthians 10:4 in the Message version states, "…the divine power smashes warped philosophies and tears down barriers erected against the truth of God." As I've previously stated, there is power in having God's Word stored in our memory banks. My transformed life is full of challenges at every turn. I need divine power and protective layers in my life.

New Challenges Reinforce Our Spiritual Dependence

From mid-2000 to mid-2010, my family experienced an empty nest, two years of care for my father-in-law in our home until his death, the heavy responsibility of my Dad's illness, his subsequent death, my retirement from the corporate world and move to full-time ministry, our four cruises for rest and relaxation, my new occupation as speaker and author, and a relocation to Hawaii. These momentous life experiences brought challenges and opportunities for spiritual dependence on God for both my family and me.

In 2016, our family and friends fell to our knees in prayer when our son, Davis, broke his neck when diving into a swimming pool. He fractured his C5 and C6 vertebrae, which often results in paraplegia. Davis did not sustain a spinal cord injury and after a four-month recovery following surgery, which fused five of his vertebrae, he returned to a normal life. We praise God. Davis is a walking miracle.

A crisis or celebration can be our excuse to fail or an opportunity to persevere. We choose. Each time I've reached out to the Lord, my attitude has changed. Thank you Lord for transformation.

My friend Joyce, walked a transformation journey that many would never begin. In 2010, when we first met, Joyce had lost 150 pounds and still had 42 to go. She did not give up and pushed onto reach her goal. Here is her story:

True Measure of Success: Joyce Ainsworth

Before and after

For many years, I played the "lose a little weight then gain it back" game. I thought I had no hope of finding real freedom or success. God used FP4H as a catalyst in my life to mold and shape me; not perfect, but healthy, whole and healed. I achieved a remarkable weight loss of 192 pounds in five years.

The Promised Land of maintenance would prove to be my greatest battle and toughest challenge. I stepped into a virtual valley of decision where I had to make healthy choices every day of my life. Some choices are easier than others and that would prove true on my health journey. Life is messy. I've sustained an injury, my sister's husband passed away, my older sister battled cancer, and my kids' actions sometimes were less than responsible. When trauma and drama is all around, it's easy to slip back into old habits and hang-ups. I need strength to make the right choice every day—not some days, but every day.

Mirrors play an important part in maintaining our appearance. The reflection in the mirror influences how we feel about ourselves. One particular day, I stood gazing into the mirror. The Lord softly spoke to my spirit: "Joyce, are you as concerned about the spiritual mirrors in your life as this physical one?" *What spiritual mirrors?* I thought. The Lord showed me The Bible, The Cross, and The Empty Tomb. The Spiritual Mirrors are a perfect reflection of how God feels about us.

The Bible: His love letter to us. He loves without reservations. He provides us freedom to make choices for ourselves. When we make poor choices, He loves us the same. God never uses His love to control us.

The Cross: God loves unconditionally and His love is sacrificial and not demanding. God loves us as flawed humans. While we are still a work in progress, He chose death on the cross and took our place.

The Empty Tomb: By His power and strength we can choose well every day—not on the days I feel like it but every day for the rest of my life. In the valley of decision, we can look into the spiritual mirrors and say, "Because of my love for You, Jesus, I choose to walk in obedience this day. Freedom is mine because of your power."

It's true that being overweight is a physical problem with a spiritual solution. Author Beth Moore wrote in *Whispers of Hope*, "Healing is found in God's Word—not just in seeking healing but in seeking Him." I've struggled to find success, love, acceptance, wisdom and guidance for many years. As I gazed in my spiritual mirror, I realized the weight kept coming back because I kept depending on my own efforts to be successful when I needed to seek Jesus first. When we seek Jesus first in all we say and do, true healing comes. He will empower us to make right choices each day.

I am still on a journey to live in and understand this place called maintenance. I continue to overcome emotional barriers and find freedom in my whole person so I can live in maintenance for a lifetime. With God's help, I know it is possible. I realize, in the land of maintenance, many of the things God is calling me to do requires a stewardship-type outlook of the body. Not in vain, but practically speaking, for a very long time, I unknowingly hid behind the truth that God only sees the heart—with all due respect—a "willful" neglect of the body is a heart issue. Hello, the spiritual mirror is talking! When I move my decision from a physical act to a spiritual act of choice, I reflect God's love with my sacrifice.

I have determined today in the valley of decision that only the limits God sets for my life will slow me down, and not anything man-made or self-made. When I close my Bible and rise to my feet, I tell the Lord my body is at His service now. I will allow the spiritual mirrors to guide my decision each day and I will see it all as an opportunity to display my love and honor for Him. Christ in us can truly be life changing. Change your mind. Change your body. Change your Life.

A Miraculous Makeover

> *Therefore, if anyone is in Christ, the new creation has come:*
> *The old has gone, the new is here!* (2 Corinthians 5:17)

Father Carl Arico addresses transformation this way in his book on prayer, A Taste of Silence: "Transformation, the process of God's recreating of our very selves, is characterized in three phases. The first phase is *simple transformation,* which takes place because of our desire and willingness to consent to changes… The second phase … is *transitional transformation,* which means that although we desire and we are active agents in our own cause, we start to feel out of control. It is a subtle change that begins to take place. The last phase is *radical transformation.* In this phase we are completely out of control, we are no longer in charge. God has taken over and is working on levels of our being we cannot get to… All the phases of transformation are not done through our strategies. They are done to us because we are open to remaining in the presence of God."

Transformation requires time with God. My pursuit of the Lord looks different each day. Some days, I pray during a run or swim. Another, I might fast with prayer. Each day, I do my best to read Scripture, work on a Bible study and read a devotion. I fill my journals with Scripture, observations, action steps and prayers. Spending time with the Lord clears off the grime built up over the past day.

Time spent with God requires changes of priorities. When I allowed the Lord to prioritize my time, I discovered spending time to strengthen myself came before serving others. Ironically, the healthier I am, the better I love and serve others.

Caring for my temple requires changes in my choices. Healthy choices are non-negotiable. I am not perfect. When I slip, I forgive myself, consider the life lesson then move on. Every day is a new day, every meal is a new meal, and every bite is a new chance to do the next right thing. I ran from the truth too many times. I need to weigh in on a scale each week. Its numbers display the truth that I need. It does not define me, but it's solid feedback.

When we care for our temple because we are filled with the presence of the Holy Spirit, we are honoring God with our body. The Holy Spirit transforms our lives and pleasing the Lord becomes our love language. We no longer need to stuff ourselves with food that does not bring true comfort or satisfaction. When we focus on Jesus, we discover nourishment that gratifies our ravenous soul. Christ endured the cross so that we could be radically transformed by His Holy Spirit. In our brokenness and beauty, forgiven and beloved, our interior and exterior begin their miraculous makeovers. The overflow of God's love in our life defines the success of our makeovers. It doesn't matter how much weight we've lost, the amount of Scriptures memorized, or Bible studies completed. Success is measured by whether or not we place Christ in first place.

During a coaching session in 2016 with one of my leaders, we discussed the radical differences from our lives before and after we started First Place 4 Health. I rolled my eyes, remembering the Helen of 2006 when I first started on the journey, resistant to change and hopeless in my obesity. Now 10 years older, I'm told I look younger than I did a decade ago. I desire to embrace the change God has planned for my life and I live a healthy lifestyle. I'm almost unrecognizable on the inside and outside.

"I wonder what changes will take place in your life over the next 10 years," my leader queried.

I chuckled with an honest skeptic's laugh. "Oh my, could there be that much more to change in my life?"

The scary reality is yes, there's plenty to change. If I am willing, He will change me. I need to practice what I preach, surrender control and allow God to take first place in every situation. I always want God to do something new in my life, so I, too, must be willing to do something new.

The world tries to tell us that sustained weight loss is impossible. I'm astounded each day by God and the strength I draw from Him. Allow God's love to be your motivation and power as you embrace weight loss God's way. What change do you need to embrace? Say yes!

Apprentice with the Master Craftsman

Will you embrace the transformation from God or will you remain unchanged?

What old habit are you clinging to that impact your health and wellness?

What new thing are you willing to do so that God can do a new thing in your life?

Prayer:

Lord, you know me. Search my heart and show me the offensive ways within. Show me the old habits I cling to. Lord I want freedom from the strongholds in my life that keep me from you. Help me recognize Your power in my life. The same power that rose Jesus from the grave. Help me live as the new creation I am in Christ. Thank you Lord for revealing to me the changes you want for my life. Transform me Lord. I desire freedom from obesity forever. Amen.

Devotions:

Galatians 5 – Freedom in Christ

Philippians 1 – A Worthy Life

Ephesians 6 – Armor of God

Philippians 2 – Do Everything Without Grumbling

Galatians 6 – What Counts is the New Creation

Appendix

Weight Loss Plans

First Place 4 Health (FP4H.com) encompasses emotional, spiritual, mental and physical health.

- Emotional: It provides support and accountability with others and investigates the root of emotional eating.

- Spiritual: It recognizes that we need God's power to restore us. We turn our will and our lives over to the care of the Lord.

- Mental: We learn, practice and reinforce healthier eating and physical activity habits. All of this changes your mind about the concept of wellness.

- Physical: We strengthen our bodies with regular activity and exercise. We rest our bodies daily and weekly. FP4H's Live IT© plan is based on the USDA's dietary guidelines and feeds the body with a balance of all food groups: fruits, vegetables, grains, lean protein, calcium-rich foods and healthy fats.

Bod 4 God (bod4god.org) teaches small simple changes will lead to a new lifestyle—a path to a new life. It is based on these components:

- Dedication: Honoring God with Your Body

- Inspiration: Motivating Yourself for Change

- Eat and Exercise: Managing Your Habits

- Team: Building Your Circle of Support

The Daniel Plan (TheDanielPlan.com) focuses on the core food groups of healthy carbs, healthy fats, healthy protein, healing spices, drinks and superfoods. It is a healthy lifestyle program founded on Biblical principles and focuses on the essentials: faith, food, fitness, focus and friends.

- Faith: God is the power and the energy behind all transformational change and includes making the lifestyle choices necessary for you to become healthy.

- Food: A healthy lifestyle program framed around abundance, not deprivation.

- Fitness: Provides guidance and encourages you to discover creative ways to enjoy exercise.

- Focus: Transforming your mind will reduce stress, improve your decision-making and memory, help you think clearer, feel better and ultimately help you to live a healthier life.

- Friends: God created us to thrive in relationship, and together we are crucial to each other's healing and success.

ChooseMyPlate.com, the USDA's food plan, emphasizes fruit, vegetable, grains, protein foods, and dairy groups. The USDA Center for Nutrition Policy and Promotion provides detailed information on choosing the right calorie level, identifying a balanced quantity of fruits, vegetables, grains, protein foods and dairy groups. (The First Place 4 Health plan is based on this plan.)

Weight Watchers (Weightwatchers.com) emphasizes seeing food as fuel for a healthy life, finding ways to move more each day, and developing skills to unlock your inner strength so you can make healthy choices for life.

Restored! Embracing Weight Loss In God's Way

Scripture Devotions to Read With Each Chapter

Spending time in God's word will strengthen your relationship with the Lord and allow time for you to grow spiritually. On your own, complete the daily devotion using SOAP. SOAP is a method to sense God when reading the Bible. Five days each week, read and then SOAP a section from the list below.

S – Scripture: Write out one verse that stands out to you.

O – Observation: Write out the "what", "where", "how" and "when" tjat you discover in the verse and the surrounding section.

A – Application: Write how you sense that God wants you to apply this observation to your life.

P – Prayer: Write a short prayer in response requesting God's help in how to obey.

Week One: SOAP Devotions for Chapter One
Romans 3 - Faith and Righteousness
John 1:1-18 – In the Beginning
Romans 5 - Life Through Christ
John 10:1-21 - The Good Shepherd and His Sheep
Romans 6 - Alive in Christ

Week Two: SOAP Devotions for Chapter Two

Acts 1 - Waiting For the Holy Spirit

Hebrews 4 - God's Promise and Your Faith

Acts 2:1-35 - Sensing God's Plan

Hebrews 5:1-14 - Jesus' Obedience

Acts 2:36-47 - Change Your Life

Week Three: SOAP Devotions for Chapter Three

1 Corinthians 1 - God's Wisdom

Luke 9:1-36 - Stop Running Away

1 Corinthians 2 - God's Spirit and God's Power

Luke 9:37-62 - The Healing Power of Jesus

1 Corinthians 3 - You are God's Temple

Week Four: SOAP Devotions for Chapter Four

1 Corinthians 4 – Everything You Need

1 Peter 1:1-13 – The Power of The Holy Spirit

1 Corinthians 5 – Spiritual Pride

1 Peter 1:14-25 – Exercise Self-Control

1 Corinthians 6 – The Temple of the Holy Spirit

Week Five: SOAP Devotions for Chapter Five

1 Timothy 4 – Our Hope is in the Living God

Psalm 139: 1-12 – God Sees Me and Knows Me

1 Timothy 5 – Don't Share in the Sins of Others

Psalm 139: 13-24 – I Am Fearfully and Wonderfully Made

1 Timothy 6 – Pursue Righteousness and a Godly Life

Week Six: SOAP Devotions for Chapter Six

Hebrews 11 – Faith in Action

Philippians 3 – Press on Toward the Goal

Hebrews 12 – No Discipline is Pleasant

Philippians 4 – All Things in God's Strength

Hebrews 13 – The Lord is My Helper

Week Seven: SOAP Devotions for Chapter Seven

Deuteronomy 29:1-15 – Renewal of God's Covenant

Matthew 4:1-11 – The Temptation of Jesus

Deuteronomy 29:16-29 – When We Lived in Egypt

Matthew 4:12-25 – The Beginning of Jesus' Ministry

Deuteronomy 30 – Choose Life or Death

Week Eight: SOAP Devotions for Chapter Eight

Isaiah 61:1-11 - Freedom for the Captives

Luke 4:1-30 – Tested in the Wilderness

Luke 4: 31-44 – Jesus Amazed People

1 Corinthians 10:1-13 – Common Temptation

1 Corinthians 10:14-33 – Not Everything is Beneficial

Week Nine SOAP: Devotions for Chapter Nine

Matthew 21:1-22 – Blessed is He

Matthew 21:23-46 – Jesus' Authority Questioned

2 Corinthians 10 – Demolish Arguments

2 Corinthians 11:1-15 – False Teachers

2 Corinthians 11:16-30 – Show My Weakness

Week Ten: SOAP Devotions for Chapter 10

Ephesians 1 – Spiritual Blessings

Ephesians 2 – By Grace You are Saved

Ephesians 3 – God's Marvelous Plan

Ephesians 4 – Unity and Maturity

Ephesians 5 – Always Give Thanks

Week Eleven: SOAP Devotions for Chapter 11

Galatians 5 – Freedom in Christ

Philippians 1 – A Worthy life

Ephesians 6 – Armor of God

Philippians 2 – Do Everything Without Grumbling

Galatians 6 – What Counts is the New Creation

Small Group Discussion Guide

This Devotion and Small Group Guide will help you to discover and apply God's Word to your life. A disciple listens for God and obeys His prompts. We receive and give encouragement when we share the journey with each other.

Each week, meet with a small group and discuss the questions provided. To get the most out of your discussions, limit the size of your group to five people. If you have six or more, break into smaller groups of three or four. The following is a suggested agenda for a 60- to 90-minute meeting.

Large Group:

5 to 15 minutes Greeting, Ice Breaker, Opening Prayer

Break into smaller groups of 3-4, then:

10 minutes   Accountability; Share progress you've each made implementing a new change.

25 minutes   Discuss Questions, Share Next Steps

15 minutes   Pray for One Another

Reconvene into one large group, then:

5 to 15 minutes Closing

Week One: Group Discussion Guide

Pray for and trust the Holy Spirit to be at work in each person present.

Passage: John 1:1-18, John 10:1-21

1. Why is it that most people are not experiencing life abundantly and to the fullest (John 10:10)?

2. Receiving Christ involves turning to God from yourself and trusting Christ to come into our lives to forgive our sins and make us what He wants us to be. Some of us might agree intellectually that Jesus Christ is the Son of God and that He died on the cross for our sins. Knowing is not enough, nor is it enough to have an emotional experience. You receive Jesus Christ by faith, as an act of the will. Are you certain that you have received Christ?

3. Chapter One ends with a prayer to receive Christ. Make certain that you have received Christ. Have everyone bow their heads and pray the prayer to themselves if they are ready to receive Christ.

   Lord Jesus, I need You. Thank You for dying on the cross for my sins. I open myself to You and receive You as my Savior and my Lord. Thank You for forgiving my sins and giving me eternal life. Teach me how to give you first plac in my life. Amen.

4. Celebrate with your group anyone who prayed the prayer for the first time.

5. What kind of impact do you dream your faith will have on your

wellness journey?

6. Share what you might have sensed or heard when you spent time in quiet listening to God as directed in Apprentice With the Master Craftsman.

Invite everyone to join in praying and asking the Lord to lead us and help us on the journey together over the next weeks.

Week Two: Group Discussion Guide

Pray for and trust the Holy Spirit to be at work in each person present.

Passage: Acts 2:37-40, Hebrews 4:14-16

1. How would you put Peter's answer in your own words and explain what it means to become a Christian? What is required? What is promised (Acts 2:38-40)?

2. Chapter Two uncovered deeply embedded lies and self-imposed limitations regarding freedom from obesity. Where does caring for your body line up in spiritual importance to prayer, weekend worship, Sabbath, Bible reading, tithing and serving others?

3. Admitting your weakness is the first step.

    *   What opinions and culture dictate your eating habits?

    *   How are you hurting yourself with food in a quest for comfort?

    *   What foods and desires are elevated above a relationship with God?

4. What will happen if you keep doing the same thing? How does that make you feel?

5. How do you think God feels when He sees you struggling (Hebrews 4:15)?

6. What do you think God wants to do for you when you struggle?

7. What will you gain if you ask God for His help with this struggle?

8. What kind of impact do you dream of that will come when you claim God's truth over your weaknesses?

Write down one area of your life that you want to bring under the Lordship of Christ in the next week. Invite everyone to join in praying asking the Lord to lead us and help us on the journey together over the next weeks.

Week Three: Group Discussion Guide

Pray for and trust the Holy Spirit to be at work in each person present. Living your life as an example of one filled with Him requires a constant relationship with Him on your part. What has helped you with the steps you decided to make last week? Share one SOAP where God showed you something new this week.

Passages: Luke 9:23-26, 1 Corinthians 2:6-16

1. What actions and attitudes are key to following Christ (Luke 9:23)?

2. What does it mean to a) deny yourself? b) take up your cross daily? c) follow Christ? d) lose your life (Luke 9-23-24)?

3. What has helped you grow in trust in God's provision for your life over the past few years?

4. What does it mean to have God's secret wisdom? How does the wisdom of God differ from the wisdom of the world (1 Corinthians 2:6-10)?

5. Chapter Three is about discovering our current situation and embracing a new plan with a willingness for change in our life. How do you feel about embracing a new plan for wellness?

6. What are two hopes, plans or dreams that you have for your life? How do your hopes, plans and dreams intersect with your wellness and God's purpose in the world?

7. Is there a better time to start following a healthy self-care plan? When and why?

8. What small step could you take in response to God's prompting based on this week's discussion?

Write down how you think God is prompting you and take a step toward obedience this week. Invite everyone to join in praying aloud together, taking time for each person to speak with the Lord to lead us and help us obey as disciples on the journey together over the next weeks.

Week Four: Group Discussion Guide

Pray for and trust the Holy Spirit to be at work in each person present. Living your life as an example of one filled with Him requires a constant relationship with Him on your part. What has helped you with the steps you decided to make last week? Share one SOAP where God showed you something new this week.

Passages: 1 Peter 1:13-16, 1 Corinthians 6:19-20

1. How has the grace given to you by Jesus changed your perspective on life (v.13)?

2. Do you consider yourself an obedient person? Why or why not?

3. Why is it important to be considered an obedient person? Do you think obedience is necessary? If not, what keeps you from embracing the need for obedience?

4. How does honoring God with your body change your perspective on obedience (1 Corinthians 6:20)?

5. Chapter Four is about establishing healthy limits in your life. What would be a benefit if you started eating within a healthy food limit?

6. What will you need to forgo or sacrifice to stay within a healthy limit?

7. Do you have the type of personality where you can live without limits and still lose or maintain your weight? Why or why not?

8. How will your life differ after a few months if you develop a habit to eat within your healthy limits?

Write down how you think God is prompting you and take a step toward obedience this week.

Invite everyone to join in praying aloud together, taking time for each person to speak with the Lord to lead us and help us obey as disciples as we journey together over the next weeks.

Week Five: Group Discussion Guide

Pray for and trust the Holy Spirit to be at work in each person present. Living your life as an example of one filled with Him requires a constant relationship with Him on your part. What has helped you with the steps you decided to make last week? Share one SOAP where God showed you something new this week.

Passages: Psalm 139:13-18, 1 Timothy 4:9-15

1. What do you look like when you compare yourself to others? Or, when you compare yourself to past failures or successes?

2. How does God see you (Psalm 139:14)? How does that differ from how you see yourself?

3. If Almighty God says you and your works (the things you do) are wonderful, do you or does anyone else have the right to disagree? Why or why not?

4. What actions do you need to take to not allow anyone to look down on you (1 Timothy 4:12-13)?

5. Chapter Five discusses cementing the healthy lifestyle changes with praise of your progress. Do you struggle with the need for perfection or the need to reach a higher goal before you celebrate? Why or why not?

6. What challenges have you overcome? What progress does God want you to celebrate today?

7. What Wellness Journey Stage listed in chapter four has been the most difficult?

8. Have you reached a stage that seems impossible and defies human ability? Is it possible that God is asking you to rely solely on Him?

Write down how God is asking you to rely solely on Him. Allow God to fight for you. Invite everyone to join in praying aloud together, taking time for each person to speak with the Father to lead us and help us obey as disciples as we journey together over the next weeks.

Week Six: Group Discussion Guide

Pray for and trust the Holy Spirit to be at work in each person present. Living your life as an example of one filled with Him requires a constant relationship with Him on your part. What has helped you with the steps you decided to make last week? Share one SOAP where God showed you something new this week.

Passages: Hebrews 11:1-6, Philippians 3:7-14

1. Who is the person or present day hero that encourages you by their faith?

2. Define faith in your own words. What is required? What is promised (Hebrews 11)?

3. How has your faith impacted your life? Your family? Your friends?

4. What does Paul's faith gain him (Philippians 3:9)?

5. Paul uses a track to help us understand our spiritual life. What actions has Paul done in his race (vv. 12-14)?

6. Chapter Six discusses the changes in attitude and lifestyle towards physical activity. Which stage do you consider yourself to be in when it comes to daily exercise? On the sidelines with no plans to join? Aware of the need to change and contemplating options? Planning your action step checking out a gym, talking with a trainer, or praying for a buddy to join you? Beginner-training two or three times a week? Maintaining a five- to six-day a week training plan? Relapsed or had a

setback and need to start over?

7. When we do something that God desires, we most often need to relinquish something we desire. What faith-filled step is God asking you to? Do you need to walk away from something or run towards something? Or modify something so you may press onto the prize for which God has called you to in Christ Jesus?

8. How will your life differ after a few months if you develop a habit of exercise?

Write down how you think God is prompting you and take a step toward obedience this week.

Invite everyone to join in praying aloud together, taking time for each person to speak with the Lord to lead us and help us obey as disciples as we journey together over the next weeks.

Week Seven: Group Discussion Guide

Pray for and trust the Holy Spirit to be at work in each person present. Living your life as an example of one filled with Him requires a constant relationship with Him on your part. What has helped you with the steps you decided to make last week? Share one SOAP where God showed you something new this week.

Passages: Matthew 4:1-11, Deuteronomy 30:11-19, 2 Corinthians 10:4

1. What life-or-death situation have you found yourself in?

2. What objections do you see in your own life which sound like the ones in verses Deuteronomy 30:11-13?

3. Where and what are the commands (vv. 14-16, 19-20)?

4. How can you live out the actions in verse 20? Why would you? How will you allow God to help you?

5. Jesus was led by the spirit into the desert to be tempted (Matthew 4:1). What were the circumstances of Jesus' temptations (vv. 3-9)? How did He overcome the temptation?

6. Chapter Seven discusses how sin often starts first in our mind. In the past, have you been able to maintain discipline in your eating and exercise habits? Why or why not?

7. When you think about how long you have renewed your thoughts compared to how long you have been on your wellness journey, is it reasonable to expect victory every time? Why or why not?

8. Focused on the future, what do you think God wants you to do next?

   a. Look for an easy way out that requires minimal change.

   b. Give up and return to comfortable old habits.

   c. Dwell on your past failures, convinced there is no hope for you.

   d. Do nothing and hope God miraculously changes you.

   e. Recognize you're in a war for life and death, blessings and curses. Fight the battle with spiritual weapons with divine power: God's word (2 Corinthians 10:4).

Write down how you think God is prompting you and take a step toward obedience this week.

Invite everyone to join in praying aloud together, taking time for each person to speak with the Lord to lead us and help us obey as disciples as we journey together over the next weeks.

Week Eight: Group Discussion Guide

Pray for and trust the Holy Spirit to be at work in each person present. Living your life as an example of one filled with Him requires a constant relationship with Him on your part. What has helped you with the steps of obedience from last week? Share one SOAP where God showed you something new this week.

Passages: Luke 4:1-13, 1 Corinthians 10:11-13

1. What is your favorite treat? When and where do you enjoy the food?

2. What emotions would you imagine Jesus experienced after forty days in the desert (Luke 4:1-2)?

3. Jesus endured three temptations from the devil. If the devil tempted you, what three areas would he focus in your life?

4. When we think we are standing firm, what could happen to us (1 Corinthians 10:12)?

5. How do the actions in 1 Corinthians 10:13 help you with your temptations?

6. Chapter Eight focuses on identifying the root when we overeat to cope with life. What habit did you uncover this week?

7. How does being in our group help you with the temptations you experience?

8. What healthy alternatives listed in chapter eight will you adopt?

Write down how you think God is prompting you and take a step toward obedience this week.

Invite everyone to join in praying aloud together taking time for each person to speak with the Lord. Ask God to strip away the sinful nature and release the fruit of His Spirit within you.

Week Nine: Group Discussion Guide

Pray for and trust the Holy Spirit to be at work in each person present. Living your life as an example of one filled with Him requires a constant relationship with Him on your part. What has helped you with the steps of obedience from last week? Share one SOAP where God showed you something new this week.

Passages: Matthew 21:18-22, 2 Corinthians 10:1-6

Note: There is one less question this week to allow extra time for praying with partners.

1. Were you taught any prayers growing up? If so, what prayers do you remember?

2. Do you go to a specific place to pray? If so, where?

3. Is there a specific person, topic or concern on which your prayer focuses?

4. How does the promise of verse 22 strengthen your perspective towards prayer (Matthew 21:18-22)?

5. Chapter Nine outlines the evolution of a prayer life: learn, praying with others, tools, disciplines and the power of God's word added to

prayer. Where do you want to focus next in your prayer life?

6. What obstacle do you desire to overcome: unbelief, doubt, idolatry, unforgiveness, doubt, anger, pride, guilt, depression, feeling unloved, addiction, despair from loss, or something else?

7. What steps will you take to strengthen your spiritual disciplines to overcome your obstacles?

Partner up and pray for each other. Ask God to strip away the obstacles and overcome any strongholds. Consider reading God's word during your prayer time: Deuteronomy 33:26-28 Psalm 21:1-5; 1 Corinthians 6:12; Ephesians 3:20-21

Week Ten: Group Discussion Guide

Pray for and trust the Holy Spirit to be at work in each person present. Living your life as an example of one filled with Him requires a constant relationship with Him on your part. What has helped you with the steps of obedience from last week? Share one SOAP where God showed you something new this week.

Passages: Ephesians 1:15-21, Ephesians 4:22-23

1. What is your favorite piece of clothing that you refuse to throw away or donate?

2. Of the things Paul is praying for the Ephesians in Chapter 1:15-21, which do you need today?

3. Where do you need God's "incomparably great power" (vv. 19) in your life?

4. What does it mean to "put off the old self" and "put on the new self" (Ephesians 4:22-23)?

5. In what areas of your life are you making progress in growing more Christ-like?

6. Chapter 10 focuses on accountability and the need for confidentiality and transparency. On a scale of one to 10, measure your willingness to be accountable to another person.

7. How would your life be different if someone prayed Ephesians 1:17-19 over you each week?

Partner up and pray for each other. Ask God to provide for the needs of the other person as discussed in question #2. Consider praying Ephesians 1:15-23 for each other.

Week Eleven: Group Discussion Guide

Pray for and trust the Holy Spirit to be at work in each person present. Living your life as an example of one filled with Him requires a constant relationship with Him on your part. What has helped you with the steps of obedience from last week?

Passages: Galatians 5:16-21, Ephesians 6:10-18, Galatians 5:22-26

1. On a scale of one to 10, how wild were you during your youth?

2. What is in conflict with each other in Galatians 5:17?

3. How can relying on God's armor help you to identify and stand up to sinful desires (Ephesians 6:11)?

4. How does the armor of God equip you defensively and offensively?

5. What piece of armor do you need most?

6. Chapter 11 focuses on the transformation. As we learn to live by His spirit, the fruits of His spirit are evidenced in our lives (Galatians 22-25). What is the biggest change you have seen in your life since placing Christ first?

Partner up and share with each other the two spiritual fruits most prominent in your life. How does that impact God's kingdom? Pray for each other to strengthen your Armor of God and allow the Fruits of the Spirit to grow stronger in your life.

Week Twelve: Group Discussion Guide

Consider a group social to celebrate your time together, including one or more of the following in your celebration:

- Everyone takes two to three minutes each to share how they've been transformed through the group's session. (Give the group members advanced notice to prepare.)

- Bring index cards (enough for each person to have two or three). Have people write on the cards anonymously what positive changes they've observed in two to three different people. Write the name of the person they are recognizing on each card. Read the cards aloud to the group.

- In a circle, one at a time, have the group recognize someone from your group who has impacted them. Each person has to pick a different person and the leader is recognized last.

- Place a chair in the center of the group. Each person takes turns sitting in the chair. The group prays for the person in the chair.

- Plan a time where you reach out and help others in the community. Ideas could include preparing and serving a meal to the less fortunate, providing transportation to the grocery store for someone who needs assistance shopping, hosting a walk at your church and inviting the community to get moving for their health, or planning some other wellness-related service opportunity.

About the Author

Helen Baratta is an author, speaker, coach, group leader, triathlete and nationally certified fitness instructor. In 2006, obese and unable to walk without pain, she surrendered to the Lord and He transformed her life. Since then, Helen has shed and maintained a 116-pound weight loss.

Now, as Director of Development for First Place 4 Health, as well as a triathlete, American Council on Exercise Certified Group Fitness Instructor, a Certified Personality Trainer, and a Trainer for Dynamic Church Planting International, Helen helps others embrace change and say "Yes" to all that God has planned.

Helen is a contributing author of five nonfiction books, including Inspire! Women's Stories of Accomplishment, Encouragement and Influence (Pennsylvania Family Publishing, 2014).

In her previous 30-year career, Helen successfully managed Health Claims and Customer Service departments for three companies (one a Fortune 500), overseeing hundreds of employees and multimillion-dollar budgets. She has a BS in Management and Consumer Studies from University of Maryland and serves on the board of Unconditional Ministries, Inc.

Helen and her husband, Vince, have two grown sons and reside in Waikoloa, Hawaii. She can be reached at Helenbaratta.com.